CW00377305

Agrarian Change in the Scottish Highlands

The role of the Highlands and Islands Development Board in the agricultural economy of the Crofting Counties

John Bryden and George Houston

GLASGOW SOCIAL AND ECONOMIC RESEARCH STUDIES

An Introduction to the Italian Economy
Kevin Allen and Andrew Stevenson

The Economics of Inflation
James A. Trevithick and Charles Mulvey

The Industrial Relations Act
A. W. J. Thomson and S. R. Engleman

Agrarian Change in the Scottish Highlands

The role of the Highlands and Islands Development Board in the agricultural economy of the Crofting Counties

John Bryden

Head of Land Development Division, Highlands and Islands Development Board

George Houston

Professor of Agricultural Economics, University of Glasgow

GLASGOW SOCIAL & ECONOMIC RESEARCH STUDIES 4

MARTIN ROBERTSON

in association with

HIGHLANDS & ISLANDS DEVELOPMENT BOARD

First published in 1976 by Martin Robertson & Co. Ltd., 17 Quick Street, London N1 8HL in association with the Highlands & Islands Development Board.

ISBN 0 85520 151 7

Printed in Scotland by John G Eccles Printers Ltd, Inverness

Preface

This book has two main purposes — to bring together selected data on the output and resources of agriculture (and the other land-based activities) in the Scottish Highlands and to describe and discuss the agricultural role of a new kind of regional development authority — the Highlands and Islands Development Board, which was established in 1965. The study thus has a limited scope and deliberately omits consideration of the effects of other policy measures and public bodies on Highland agriculture.

The origins of the book will help to explain its form and approach. Both authors have been associated in different capacities and for different periods with the Land Division of the HIDB. At the suggestion of the Board Member responsible for this division (Mr Prophet Smith) it was decided to bring together in one volume certain basic data on Highland agriculture, an account of the Board's own activities in this sector and a discussion of the broad principles on which these activities might be based. From the outset it was agreed that at no stage would the aim be to produce a report or policy document for formal approval and adoption by the Board. The nearest analogy would be a kind of 'green paper' made available as widely as possible for discussion by all those with an interest in the agriculture and land economy of the Highlands and Islands. Once the manuscript was completed it was agreed by those responsible for the Glasgow Series that its content and scope made it suitable for inclusion in the series.

It will become obvious that the authors are committed to the view that the HIDB should have an active regional role in the development of agriculture. The extent to which such a commitment, combined with an involvement in some of the activities under discussion, has prevented a balanced approach to the subject is for the reader to judge. The authors have tried to present as fairly as possible the less as well as the more successful aspects of the Board's agricultural activities. The Board itself has encouraged us to take this approach but responsibility for the views expressed rests with the authors and no one else. Our thanks and acknowledgments are due to many persons, however, and in particular to colleagues on the staff of the HIDB, DAFS, the University of Glasgow and other public bodies and to our secretaries, Mrs Braid and Mrs Campbell.

Contents

Chapter Contents

List of Tables

List of Maps and Diagrams

Authors' Note

The definition of regions has always been a vexed question in regional science. In the Highlands and Islands region the terminology has become more confused since the local government reorganisation of 1975 which created a 'Highland Region' and a Highland Regional Council — which, however, only covers a part of the Highlands and Islands as defined in Section 1(2) of the Highlands and Islands Development (Scotland) Act 1965. Moreover, Section 1(2) of the 1965 Act was amended in 1975 to extend the area covered by the Highlands and Islands Development Board to include Bute, Arran, Nairn, Cromdale and Grantown-on-Spey. We have used the 1965 definition of the Highlands and Islands which is coterminous with the Crofting Counties since most of our data refer to the period before these administrative changes took place. Thus we use the terms 'Highlands and Islands', 'Crofting Counties', 'Highlands region', 'Board Area' synonymously and any references to 'the region' should be taken to mean the Highlands and Islands.

A similar terminological difficulty arises with the HIDB itself which is often popularly referred to as the 'Highland Board', the 'Development Board', or simply the 'Board'. We have used these terms interchangeably in the text, along with the acronym HIDB, to refer to the Highlands and Islands Development Board.

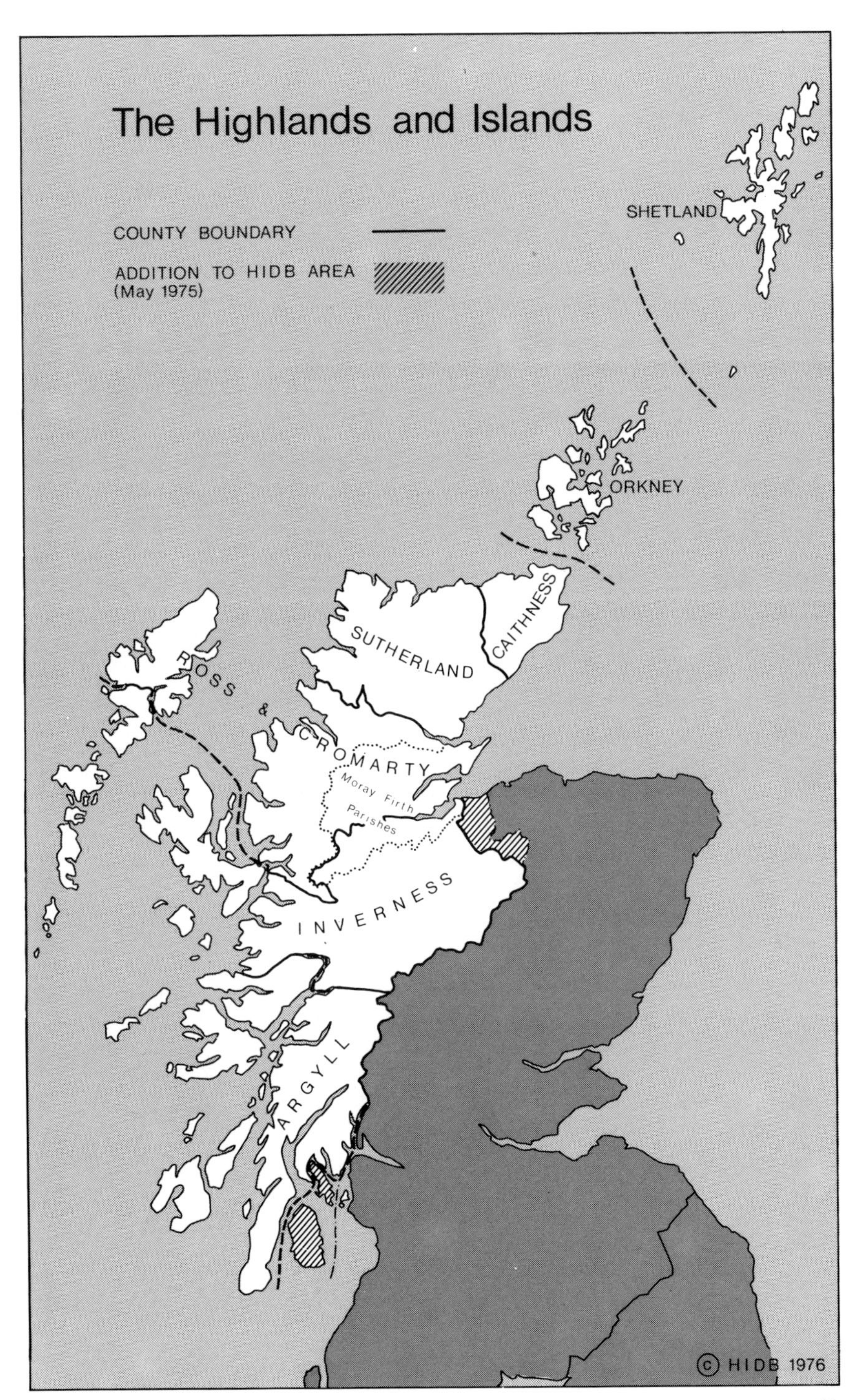
The Highlands and Islands
COUNTY BOUNDARY
ADDITION TO HIDB AREA
(May 1975)
SHETLAND
ORKNEY
CAITHNESS
SUTHERLAND
ROSS
&
CROMARTY
Moray Firth
Parishes
INVERNESS
ARGYLL
© HIDB 1976

Abbreviations used in text

DAFS	Department of Agriculture and Fisheries for Scotland
DTI	Department of Trade and Industry
FEOGA	Fonds Européen d'Orientation et de Garantie Agricole. (Also known as EAGGF: The European Agricultural Guidance and Guarantee Fund)
HFRO	Hill Farming Research Organisation
HIDB	Highlands and Islands Development Board
Int J Biometeor	International Journal of Biometeorology
R & D	Research and Development
SAOS	Scottish Agricultural Organisation Society
SAE	Scottish Agricultural Economics
SGM	Scottish Geographical Magazine
SIC	Standard Industrial Classification
SMD	Standard Man-Day
Trans H & A Soc Scot.	Transactions of the Highland and Agricultural Society of Scotland

Note on Measurements

Imperial rather than metric units have normally been used in the text, most source material being in imperial units. Some important conversion factors are:

1 acre	= 0.4047 hectare
2½ acres	= 1 hectare approx.
250 acres	= 1 square kilometre approx.
1 UK ton/acre	= 2.5107 tonnes per hectare
1 UK cwt/acre	= 125.53 Kg per hectare
1 foot	= 30 cms = 0.3048 metre
1 hoppus foot (timber)	= 0.0361 cubic metres
1 cubic metre	= 27.7361 hoppus feet

PART 1. The Factual Background

Introduction

Part 1 presents the factual background to the agricultural and land use problems of the Highlands and Islands. Scottish data and historical data have been introduced where they seemed relevant to the problems under consideration but the emphasis is on the contemporary situation within the Highlands. As the region is by no means homogeneous in its resources or potential, sub-regional data are also discussed wherever relevant and available. As with all such studies a balance has had to be struck between excessive detail and clarity of presentation. Chapter One deals with agricultural production, output and incomes with emphasis on trends as they compare with Scotland and on the dual structure of the agricultural industry in the region. Chapter Two is concerned with broader questions of rural land use, ownership and control with emphasis on the pattern of land use in the region and the historical, environmental and institutional factors which have influenced and shaped this pattern. The potential for land improvement and development is also discussed. Chapter Three moves on to a discussion of manpower and productivity and completes this factual assessment of output and resources. It includes consideration of capital investment in Highland agriculture.

CHAPTER 1

Agricultural Production, Output and Incomes

Section 1: **Trends since 1870**

Agriculture in the Highlands,[1] as in Scotland and indeed all other European countries, has been declining in relative economic importance for many years. Within the crofting counties it now employs 10 per cent of the occupied population, compared with about 25 per cent fifty years ago and roughly 40 per cent in the 1870's. In terms of output and incomes, agriculture's share of Highland economic activity has been rather less than its share of employment (and is currently probably around 8 per cent) but by geographical area, and more debatably in broad social and cultural terms, the relative importance of agriculture within the Highlands may be valued more highly; in landward areas[2] it employs one in six of the working population and on many islands and in some mainland areas it plays a crucial role in local income generation and hence the maintenance of settlement patterns.

While the Highlands and Islands as a whole ceased to be predominantly agricultural long before the economic changes of recent years, it still sustains a society with a different rural/urban balance to the rest of Scotland. As Table 1-1 shows, agriculture has been roughly three times as important in the Highlands as in Scotland — measured in terms of occupational structure. Moreover, a greater proportion of people in the crofting counties engage in part-time or spare-time farming activity (see page 9) and others occupy areas of land where this would be possible.

The decline in the Highlands' share of the Scottish economy up till the 1960s is well known — as are signs that this decline has been halted or at least slowed down in the past 10-15 years (see Table 1-2). What is not so widely recognised is that similar trends have taken place in the contribution of the crofting counties to Scottish agriculture. As Table 1-2 reveals,

1 In what follows the 'Highlands', the 'Highland region' and the 'Crofting Counties' are synonymous terms and refer to the counties of Argyll, Caithness, Inverness, Orkney, Ross and Cromarty, Shetland and Sutherland.

2 Landward areas exclude conurbations and cities, large and small burghs.

Table 1-1. Agricultural Employment as a Percentage of Occupied Population

	In Scotland %	*In the Highlands* %
1871	16.5	40.5
1911	7.5	23.6
1931	7.3	22.6
1961	5.3	15.5
1971	2.9	9.9

Source: The above figures are based on the decennial census; an explanatory note is contained in Appendix 1A.

Table 1-2. Occupied Population in Scotland and the Highlands and Islands

	Total occupied population in the Highlands as a percentage of Scotland	*Population occupied in agriculture: the Highlands as a percentage of Scotland*
1871	9.7	23.9
1911	7.3	23.1
1931	5.7	17.5
1961	4.9	14.4
1971	5.0	14.4

Source: See note to Table 1-1.

Highland farming in 1961 employed around 14 per cent of the Scottish agricultural population compared with nearly 24 per cent one hundred years ago. Data on farm output is less reliable but on a very broad and rough estimate the Highlands' share of Scottish farm output over the same period fell from about 20 per cent[3] to 11 per cent. Between 1961 and 1971 the secular decline of the Highlands appears to have been slowed down in the agricultural sector as well as elsewhere.[4]

These broad trends in employment and output, although only a rough guide, suggest that if there was a 'Highland problem' in the early 1960s requiring a regional approach, then it included a farming problem with similar regional characteristics. By the 1970s it seems that the nature of any problem might have changed and that a difference in trends within the region could have acquired more importance.

During the past twenty years or so, data on farm output have become more comprehensive and reliable and will be used later in this chapter for a discussion of recent trends. For a longer term picture we must rely on cruder indicators than are now available. Diagrams 1 and 2 illustrate

3 Based on calculations made for *c.* 1885 by J R A Cumming.

4 See next section.

changes in crop acreages and livestock numbers in the crofting counties expressed as a percentage of Scottish totals. Although the downward trend does not persist for all included items in all periods (see, for instance, the relative rise of sheep numbers in the 1940s) the overall impression is that of a long term decline since the end of the last century. Relative changes in other products and in yields would not alter that broad picture.

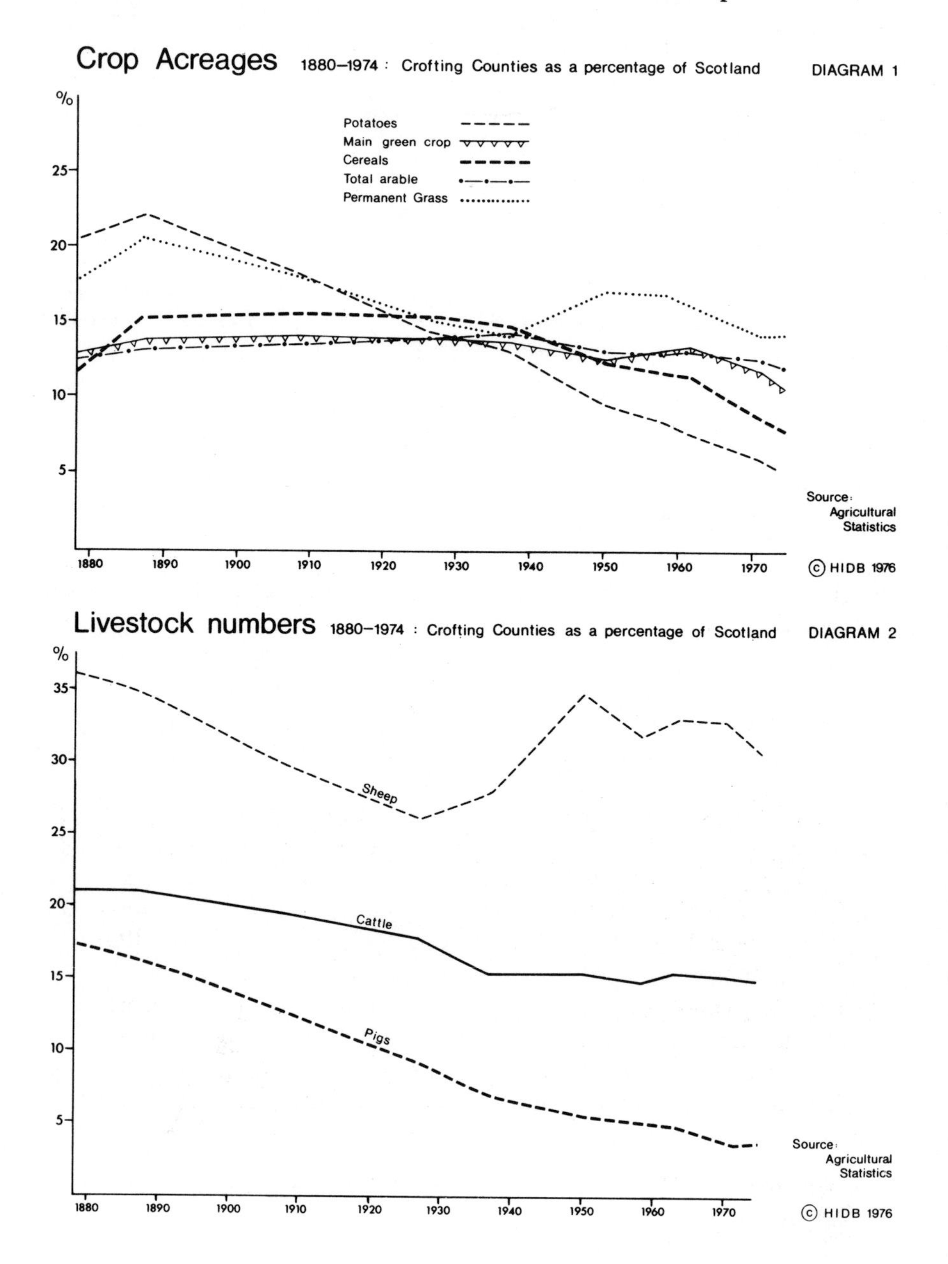

It is no purpose of this study to argue that, because of these trends over the last century or so, agriculture is no longer important to the future development of the Highlands. On the contrary we have already remarked on the regional implications of some of the data and believe that partly because of the consequences of decline, as well as for other reasons, a positive attitude towards the farming sector must be taken by a regional development agency. That attitude, however, must be based on an objective assessment of the industry's role and a detailed examination of recent trends in its output, income and use of resources. Moreover, as differences within the region may have become relatively more important in recent years, data on the geographical and structural pattern of output must also be examined. What follows is an attempt to summarise the best information available on these indicators and to provide evidence on recent sub-regional and structural changes.

Section 2: **Agricultural Output and Incomes**

Changes in the level of output of Highland agriculture and in its share of Scottish farm output have been officially calculated for selected years since the end of the last war; changes in the composition of that output have also been estimated and indicate how different types of farming have been increasing or decreasing in importance within the region.

Various terms have been used to describe different measurements of the 'output' of Scottish agriculture.[5] For the purpose of this study, the term gross output has been used to describe the value of products sold off the 'Highland farm', a substantial part of which is bought by other farmers outside the Highlands. Complete consistency in treatment of all the data in any one year (and *a fortiori* over a period) is impracticable, but gross output is, as near as possible, equal to the total value of sales from the Highland farm inclusive of price subsidies, various sundry receipts and production grants and including an adjustment for annual changes in the value of growing crops and livestock.

The most recent official estimates of the gross output (so defined) of Highland agriculture are for 1971-72 when the value was £37,510,000 or almost exactly 11 per cent of gross output in Scotland as a whole. (See Table 1-3). Sheep (including wool) accounted for 30 per cent of Highland output compared with 12 per cent in Scotland as a whole; cattle were also marginally more important, 36 per cent of output in the Highlands compared with 32 per cent in Scotland.[6]

5 For a technical discussion see the article in *Scottish Agricultural Economics*, 1975 by A M Mackenzie, P C Martin and E R Scarlett entitled 'Agricultural Output of Scotland by Regions 1971/72'. Much of what follows is based on this and earlier articles on this theme in this annual publication. But responsibility for the use made of the data belongs to the authors of this book.

6 These include production grants which are excluded from the percentages given in Table 1-3.

A direct comparison of gross output in 1971-72 with earlier estimates is seriously hampered by changes in sources and methods of calculation but it seems certain that over the period 1951-52 to 1971-72 a significant decline occurred in the share of Scottish output coming from the Highland farm. The extent of that decline cannot be given precisely in terms of any one definition of output, but compared with the figure of 11 per cent mentioned above, the value of Highland gross output in 1961-62 was about 11.3 per cent and in 1951-52 about 13 per cent of the value of Scottish output in those years.

Table 1-3. Value of Agricultural Output in Scotland and the Crofting Counties 1971-72

	Scotland		Crofting Counties	
	£'000	*% Distribution of Total Output*	*£'000*	*% Distribution of Total Output*
Total Output	282,647	100.0	25,867	100.0
Farm Crops:[a] Total	44,592	15.8	1,974	7.6
Wheat	4,728	1.7	221	0.9
Barley	20,894	7.4	1,045	4.0
Oats	3,515	1.2	142	0.5
Potatoes	14,179	5.0	689	2.7
Sugar beet	1,047	0.4	—	—
Other crops	229	0.1	—123	—0.5
Livestock: Total	147,190	52.1	16,408	63.5
Fat cattle and calves	71.267	25.2	3,259	12.6
Fat sheep and lambs	24,439	8.7	2,091	8.1
Fat pigs	20,562	7.3	741	2.9
Table poultry	12,490	4.4	141	0.5
Store cattle and calves[b]	11,240	4.0	5,451	21.1
Store sheep and lambs[b]	3,680	1.3	4,313	16.7
Other livestock[c]	3,512	1.2	412	1.6
Livestock Products: Total	77,374	27.4	6,831	26.4
Milk and milk products[a]	57,631	20.4	4,232	16.4
Eggs — for food	14,795	5.3	1,017	3.9
Wool[d]	4,027	1.4	1,355	5.2
Other livestock products[e]	921	0.3	227	0.9
Horticulture: Total	11,394	4.0	207	0.8
Vegetables	5,277	1.9	79	0.3
Fruit	2,563	0.9	77	0.3
Flowers and nursery stock	3,554	1.2	51	0.2
Sundry Output: Total	2,097	0.7	447	1.7
Sundry Receipts[f]	6,653		1,033	
Production Grants[g]	28,386		6,875	
Work in progress:[h]				
Change due to cost	+16,874		+2,965	
Change due to volume	+5,881		+770	
Gross Output	340,441		37,510	

Notes:

a Includes receipts from crops sold off farms and subsequently bought back for feed or seed but excludes deficiency payments on retained cereals and compensation payments on unsold potatoes.

b Value of net transfers into or out of region but excludes imports of Irish cattle and net movements of young calves of which Scotland is a net importer from England.

c Includes rabbits and game, exports of breeding animals and the value of net transfers into or out of the region of day-old chicks.

d Clip wool only: value of skin wool is included in the value of fat sheep.

e Include sales of eggs for hatching.

f Deficiency payments on retained cereals, PMP compensation payments, co-op society dividends and other miscellaneous receipts.

g Hill livestock, calf and beef cow subsidies and other non capital production grants.

h Closing level minus opening level each valued at estimated cost.

Source: MacKenzie A M *et al*, SAE Vol XXV, 1975.

Table 1-4. Crofting Counties as a Share of Scottish Crop Acreages and Livestock Numbers — June Census

	1958 %	*1963* %	*1968* %	*1973* %
Tillage area	11.80	11.77	10.21	8.68
of which:				
cereals	11.86	11.57	9.80	8.36
wheat	2.37	2.70	7.47	3.42
barley	4.71	5.17	5.06	6.22
oats	15.02	18.03	20.14	20.15
turnips	13.01	12.36	12.33	10.61
potatoes	8.70	7.42	7.09	5.59
vegetables	1.49	1.39	1.03	1.08
soft fruit	1.00	1.07	2.42	3.13
Grass (for mowing)	14.39	14.53	15.53	16.93
(not for mowing)	16.99	16.27	16.57	14.90
Dairy cattle	7.15	6.34	5.92	5.94
Beef cattle	20.55	20.44	19.81	17.81
Sheep	31.78	32.22	32.90	32.13
Pigs	5.05	4.49	3.64	3.84
Poultry	15.79	11.00	6.59	2.41

Note:
A change in the basis of the data took place between 1968 and 1973 but will not significantly affect the table except in the case of sheep where the decline shown between 1968 and 1973 is almost certainly the result of the change in the census basis.

Source: Based on DAFS Agricultural Statistics.

The small extent of the decrease in the period 1961-62 to 1971-72 requires special comment. In physical terms the Highlands' share of Scottish livestock numbers was declining significantly in this period (see Table 1-4) but in value terms two factors offset most of this decrease: production grants of special significance to the Highlands increased in relative importance in the period and the price of those products (sheep and cattle) which are more important to the Highlands also rose relative to the general price level for farm commodities.

In general terms, and taking the post-war period as a whole, it is clear that the long term trends discussed in the previous section continued up till the 1960s but there is evidence that from 1961 to 1971 the Highlands' share (in value terms) of Scottish farm output declined only slightly and almost certainly at a lower rate than in the past. Although the region's share of Scottish cereal acreage continued to decline in this period, the difference in crop yields was narrowed — See Tables 1-4 and 1-5.

Table 1-5. Crop Yields in Scotland and the Crofting Counties

	Scotland					*Crofting Counties*				
	1958	*1959*	*1963*	*1968*	*1973*	*1958*	*1959*	*1963*	*1968*	*1973*
Wheat[a]	25.7	30.9	27.8	33.5	38.4	n.a.	25.9	30.9	36.9	36.2
Barley[a]	26.2	28.9	27.0	28.9	34.9	n.a.	22.4	27.0	28.0	32.5
Oats[a]	19.2	20.9	20.6	22.3	29.5	n.a.	15.2	17.3	19.5	24.8
Potatoes[b]	6.8	9.3	7.3	9.4	11.7	n.a.	7.2	6.6	n.a.	n.a.
Turnips[b]	18.5	17.6	18.8	21.9	24.8	n.a.	16.0	17.3	19.2	18.7
Hay[a]	33.2	31.7	36.8	40.8	42.0	n.a.	20.9	26.9	34.1	38.0

Notes:

a Yield in cwts/acre

b Yield in tons/acre

n.a. Not available

Source: DAFS Agricultural Statistics

Alongside the downward long-term trend in the Highlands' share of Scottish farm production has been a change in the composition of that output. Milk, pigs and poultry products have all declined in relative importance while cattle, sheep and wool have increased. By 1971-72 these last three commodities accounted for 66 per cent of the value of gross output in the Highlands compared with about 58 per cent ten years earlier.[7]

So far, most of our discussion has been in terms of gross output, defined earlier. The term net output is conventionally used to describe the value of an industry's output after deductions have been made from gross output to allow for its purchases from other industries or abroad. The net output of Highland agriculture is thus the gross output minus purchases of machinery, fertilisers, feedstuffs and other inputs.[8] It represents the value placed on the contribution which farmers and farmworkers make to the Highland

7 The incidence of production grants in the definition of output complicates this kind of calculation. The above percentages are approximate figures only.

8 Including purchases of agricultural products from non-Highland farming and (for technical reasons) of cereals bought from Highland farmers. For the specialist reader it may be noted that various adjustments (eg for interest on borrowed working capital for landlord-type and tenant-type maintenance and depreciation) have been deliberately omitted, either because data were not available or because the net effect would not significantly change the picture presented here; estimates of regional net output and income must be regarded as very approximate.

economy and, by definition, is equal to the incomes received by those who work in or own resources used in agriculture in the region. Generally speaking, estimates of agricultural net output are likely to be even less reliable than gross output and this is particularly true when applied to regional data. An official estimate for net output as such is not published but from relevant data in 1971-72 may be estimated for the Highlands at about £17 million. The inputs used by Highland farmers are not radically different from other Scottish farmers, although as Table 1-6 shows, there is a different emphasis on certain items and comment is made in Chapter 3 on aspects of these differences.

Table 1-6. Estimates of the Main Farm Costs in Scotland and the Crofting Counties 1971-72

	Column 1 *Scotland*	*Column 2* *Crofting Counties*	*Column 3* *(Column 2 as percentage of Column 1)*
	£m.	£m.	%
Labour — Total	50.05	5.42	10.8
Gross Rent[a]	14.09	1.17	8.3
Interest	6.00	0.67	11.2
Machinery — Depr and repairs	35.38	6.23	17.6
Other	13.75	2.59	18.8
Total	49.13	8.82	18.0
Feedingstuffs	43.69	2.90	6.6
Seeds	6.10	0.51	8.4
Fertiliser and lime (gross)	36.26	3.61	10.0
Livestock[b]	17.10	1.21	7.1
Miscellaneous	21.24	2.79	13.1

Notes:

a Rent of tenanted farms and imputed rent of owner-occupied farms less private share of farmhouse and benefit value of cottages with an addition for interest on tenants' improvements.

b At the Scottish level this item relates to Irish store cattle and day old chicks, calves from England and Wales and expenses of inter-farm sales. The figure for the Crofting Counties, however, takes account of inter-regional as well as inter-country transfers.

Source: As for Table 1-3.

As the net output data indicate, the total agricultural income of those involved in Highland farming in 1971-72 was probably about £17 million. Of this, about £5½ million was received as wages, under £1 million as net rent (including imputed rent on owner-occupied farms) and about £10 or £11 million as the net income of farmers (including crofters). The number of persons obtaining *some* of their income from farming activities in the Highlands was probably over 16,000 in 1971-72 but the number of farmers or farmworkers working full-time in the industry was about half of this figure. The number of regular full-time farmworkers in 1971 was returned as 4,100, the number of part-time workers as 1,356 and seasonal casual workers as 828. In the 1971 population census 10,650 persons were returned as employed in agriculture and horticulture. In the same year it was estimated that there were 3,117 full-time farm units[9] in the Crofting Counties, 2,573 part-time units[10] and 6,998 spare-time units.[11] It may be said that there was the equivalent of about 11,000 persons employed in Highland agriculture in 1971-72, under half of them as employees, the remainder as self-employed. If we divide the total agriculture income of the Highlands (excluding rents) by 11,000 the income per head works out at roughly £1,500 per annum in 1971-72. This was probably about 20-25 per cent less than a similar Scottish figure but these estimates must be regarded as very approximate. Available data on earnings of full-time workers suggest little significant differences between the Highlands and the rest of Scotland.[12] The main reasons for the lower income per person are probably to be found in the greater importance of part-time activity,[13] the greater dependence on occupiers' labour input[14] and the smaller size of farm business. In terms of standard man-days, the average size of full-time holding in the Highlands is about 70 per cent of the Scottish figure.[15]

Section 3: **The Geographical and Structural Pattern of Production**[16]

The agriculture of the Highlands has up till now been treated as a single unit. While the extent of any disaggregation within this study must obviously be limited, to rely solely on the concept of the 'Highland farm' would conceal wide differences within the region and could give a misleading picture, even in broad terms. This section, therefore, presents data on the types of farming which are predominant within the region, on the localisation of production and on the size structure of Highland farming.

Farm Types

The dominance of cattle and sheep within Highland agriculture has already been mentioned and is reflected in any analysis by farm type.[17] The standard categories for such an analysis include ten type groups of which three are relatively more important in the Highlands than in Scotland as a

9 i.e. with over 250 standard man days.

10 i.e. with 100-249 standard man days.

11 i.e. with 26-100 standard man days.

12 Based on information from DAFS.

13 In the Crofting Counties, part-time and casual workers are relatively more important (see Chapter 3) and part-time and spare-time units represent a very much higher proportion of all holdings. Whereas the Highlands account for only one-seventh of all full-time units in Scotland, they contain nearly half the part-time and over two-thirds of the spare-time holdings.

14 See Chapter 3, page 76

15 See page 23

whole. These are hill sheep farms, upland farms (mainly cattle and sheep) and rearing with arable farms which in 1970 accounted respectively for 17, 37 and 12[18] per cent of the labour requirements on full-time Highland farms compared with Scottish percentages of 5, 15 and 11. As Table 1.7 shows, the relative importance of different farm types varies widely between counties, a general characteristic which is reflected in much of the data presented in this section.

One methodological point needs to be made at this stage. The most obvious and convenient units to use in discussing the geographical distribution of farm types (or farm output) would be the old administrative counties. Official statistics have normally been presented in county totals and various standard methods of analysis could be applied to that data. Within the Highlands, however, several counties show very wide variations in agricultural activity with some clearly defined localities reflecting specific environmental (and other) conditions. The most obvious examples are Inverness and Ross and Cromarty; both include parts of the fertile Moray Firth area, large parts of the central and much less productive hinterland, and several islands on the West Coast. The use of parish statistics would give a much more accurate picture of the localisation of production and of different types of farms (although some parishes are large and diverse in character) but such statistics are not so readily available in suitable form. A compromise has therefore been struck. Parish statistics have been used to construct dot maps showing the distribution of labour requirements, cattle and sheep throughout the Highlands. In addition, tables have been constructed showing county totals of farm type groups of man-days, hill cows and ewes supplemented with separate figures for those Moray Firth parishes which are within the counties of Inverness and Ross and Cromarty.[19] This approach has its deficiencies but it should go some way to meet one of the main objectives of this part of our study which is to reveal major differences of a broad kind which could be relevant to determining a varied programme of agricultural development by a regional development agency today.

The distribution of different farm type groups throughout the Highlands

16 Much of the extraction and compilation of data for this section was carried out by D MacLennan, the dot maps were prepared by J Watt and DAFS provided basic data. The year 1970 was the latest for which comprehensive data were available.

17 The method of classifying holdings is described in Agricultural Statistics, 1970, Scotland, Page 77.

18 These are not strictly comparable with published 1970 statistics. The difference does not affect the general picture.

19 These are the parishes of Tain, Tarbat, Fearn, Nigg, Logie Easter, Kilmuir Easter, Rosskeen, Alness, Kiltearn, Dingwall, Fodderty, Contin, Urray, Avoch, Killearnan, Knockbain, Cromarty, Resolis, Rosemarkie, Urquhart, Kirkhill, Kiltarlity, Kilmorack, Petty, Inverness and Bona, and Ardersier. As the map at the front shows, several of these parishes extend into the less productive hinterland so this differentiation does not quite provide a separation of the more fertile land from the rest.

has been analysed in terms of man hours and is summarised in Tables 1.7, 1.8 and 1.9. Several points are immediately obvious from Table 1.7: the virtual absence of hill sheep farms in Caithness, Orkney and the Moray Firth parishes and of arable and cropping farms in all areas outside the Moray Firth parishes, the general dominance of the two hill farm types (hill sheep and upland) modified by areas of dairy farming particularly in Argyll, Orkney and Shetland, and finally, the stark contrast between the Moray Firth parishes and the remainder of the counties of Inverness and Ross and Cromarty.

Table 1.8 reveals that half the man hours allocated to hill sheep farms in the Highlands are in Argyll while over half the man hours on upland farms are in Caithness, Orkney and the Moray Firth parishes; the last area accounts for 90 per cent of the arable and cropping allocation.

Finally, Table 1.9 distributes all the man hours between the various 'cells' thus showing (in crude terms) the relative importance of groups defined both by type and location.

Localisation of Production

Adopting a slightly different approach which ignores farm type classification as such and uses standard man days as a proxy for output, Map One shows the geographical distribution of farm output throughout the Highlands and Islands. The concentration of production in Orkney in the north-east of Caithness and in the Moray Firth area is obvious; together these areas probably account for about 50 per cent of the output of Highland agriculture (see Table 1.10) and if the more productive parts of Southern Argyll were added the proportion would rise to over 60 per cent.

Maps 2 and 3 show the distribution of cattle (beef and dairy) and sheep within the region; they indicate that while cattle tend to be concentrated in much the same way as standard man-days sheep are distributed more evenly over the area. This is also reflected in Table 1.10 which shows that while Caithness, Orkney and the Moray Firth parishes contain almost exactly 50 per cent of the hill cows they include only one-sixth of the ewes. Over large areas of the Highlands the provision of rough grazing for sheep is the only contribution the land makes to agricultural production;[20] it is the most extensive form of farm enterprise in the region.

20 Excluding venison in this definition.

Table 1-7. Farm Structure in the Crofting Counties Distribution of man Full-time Holdings, 1970

	Argyll %	*Caithness* %	*Orkney* %	*Sutherland* %	*Shetland* %	*Ross and Cromarty*[a] %	*Inverness*[a] %	*Moray Firth Parishes* %	*Crofting Counties* %
Hill Sheep	32.8	2.5	0.1	38.3	42.9	47.7	35.6	1.7	17.4
Upland	32.7	55.8	66.9	29.9	23.2	36.3	43.6	12.3	37.1
Rearing with arable	1.5	27.3	7.0	15.3	6.0	6.9	6.8	20.0	11.7
Rearing with intensive livestock	1.5	0.4	2.1	1.3	—	—	1.4	2.8	1.3
Arable, rearing and feeding	—	0.6	0.3	0.5	—	—	0.8	17.8	3.4
Cropping	0.1	1.1	0.1	5.2	—	—	4.2	30.7	8.4
Dairy	32.4	11.7	21.4	9.6	27.9	6.9	5.1	11.9	18.0
Horticulture	0.2	—	—	—	—	1.3	1.8	3.9	1.3
Poultry	—	0.2	1.8	—	—	1.0	0.8	2.0	0.9
Pigs	0.2	0.4	0.4	—	—	—	—	2.0	0.7
	100.0	100.0	100.0	100.0	100.0	100.0	100.0	100.0	100.0

Note: a Excludes Moray Firth parishes.

Source: Calculated by D. MacLennan from DAFS Statistics.

Table 1-8. Localisation of farm types by crofting county By allocated man hours Full-time Holdings, 1970

	Argyll %	*Caithness* %	*Orkney* %	*Sutherland* %	*Shetland* %	*Ross and Cromarty*[a] %	*Inverness*[a] %	*Moray Firth Parishes* %	
Hill Sheep	50.6	1.9	0.01	9.3	3.7	7.3	24.7	2.4	100.00
Upland	23.6	20.0	27.2	3.4	0.9	2.6	14.2	8.1	100.00
Rearing with arable	3.5	31.0	9.0	5.5	0.8	1.6	7.0	41.7	100.00
Rearing with intensive livestock	3.1	4.3	24.1	4.1	—	—	12.8	51.7	100.00
Arable, rearing and feeding	—	2.3	1.2	0.6	—	—	3.0	92.9	100.00
Cropping	0.2	1.8	0.1	2.6	—	—	6.0	89.3	100.00
Dairy	48.3	8.6	18.0	2.3	2.3	1.0	3.4	16.1	100.00
Horticulture	4.7	—	—	—	—	2.7	16.8	75.7	100.00
Poultry	—	3.1	30.0	—	—	3.0	23.7	53.5	100.00
Pigs	6.5	8.4	9.0	—	—	—	—	77.3	100.00

Note: a Excludes Moray Firth Parishes.

Source: as for Table 1-7.

Table 1-9. Percentage of Total allocated man hours by farm type and crofting county (on full-time holdings), 1970

	Argyll %	Caithness %	Orkney %	Sutherland %	Shetland %	Ross and Cromarty[a] %	Inverness[a] %	Moray Firth Parishes %	
Hill Sheep	8.8	0.3	—	1.6	0.6	1.3	4.3	0.4	
Upland	8.8	7.4	10.1	1.3	0.3	1.0	5.3	3.0	
Rearing with arable	0.4	3.6	1.1	0.6	0.1	0.2	0.8	9.0	
Rearing with intensive livestock	—	0.1	0.3	0.1	—	—	0.2	0.7	
Arable, rearing and feeding	—	0.1	—	—	—	—	0.1	3.1	
Cropping	—	0.2	—	0.2	—	—	0.5	7.5	
Dairy	8.7	1.6	3.2	0.4	0.4	0.2	0.6	2.9	
Horticulture	0.1	—	—	—	—	—	0.2	1.0	
Poultry	—	—	0.3	—	—	—	0.1	0.5	
Pigs	—	0.1	0.1	—	—	—	—	0.5	
	26.8	13.3	15.1	4.2	1.5	2.7	12.0	24.4	100.00

Note: a Excludes Moray Firth Parishes.
Source: as for Tables 1-7 and 1-8.

Table 1.10. Distribution of Land, Manpower Requirements, Cattle and Sheep by County,[a] 1970

Area	*Column 1* *Percentage of total acreage*[b]	*Column 2* *Percentage of standard man-days*	*Column 3* *Percentage of hill cows*	*Column 4* *Percentage of ewes*
Moray Firth parishes	8.0	20.2	13.8	5.7
Caithness	5.0	12.2	14.8	8.3
Orkney	2.5	15.4	21.2	2.4
Argyll	22.1	22.2	23.3	31.5
Inverness[a]	25.5	15.3	17.3	23.4
Ross and Cromarty[a]	17.5	5.5	3.4	10.5
Sutherland	15.0	5.0	4.3	8.7
Shetland	4.4	4.3	2.0	9.5
	100	100	100	100

Notes:

a The Moray Firth parishes are listed separately and the figures for Inverness and Ross and Cromarty exclude them.

b In this table total acreage includes common grazings; as parish data for common grazings are not available in suitable form the total acreages used in calculating entries for the Moray Firth and parts of Inverness and Ross and Cromarty are approximate estimates.

Source: Based on data supplied by DAFS.

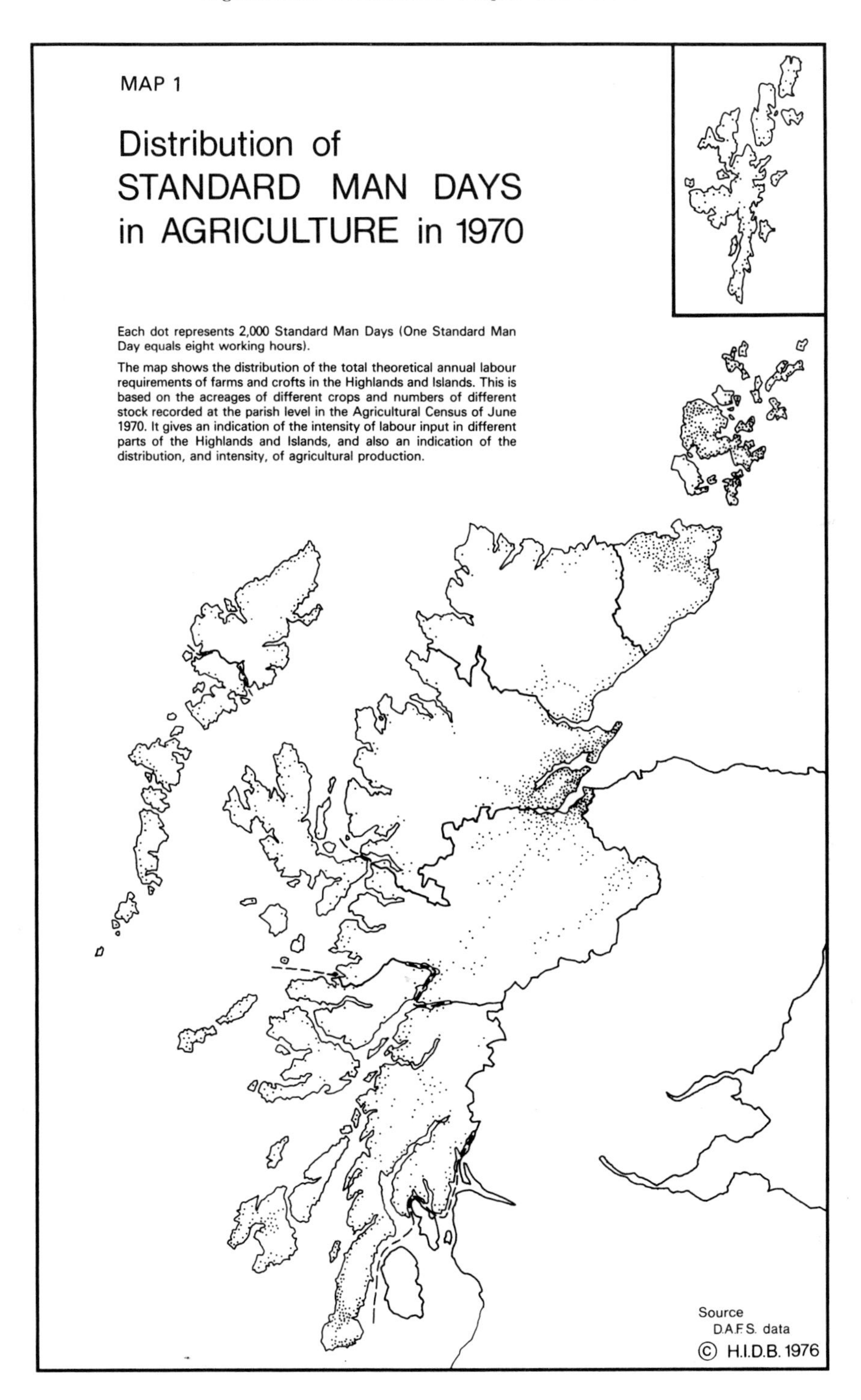
MAP 1
Distribution of
STANDARD MAN DAYS
in AGRICULTURE in 1970
Each dot represents 2,000 Standard Man Days (One Standard Man Day equals eight working hours).
The map shows the distribution of the total theoretical annual labour requirements of farms and crofts in the Highlands and Islands. This is based on the acreages of different crops and numbers of different stock recorded at the parish level in the Agricultural Census of June 1970. It gives an indication of the intensity of labour input in different parts of the Highlands and Islands, and also an indication of the distribution, and intensity, of agricultural production.
Source
D.A.F.S. data
© H.I.D.B. 1976

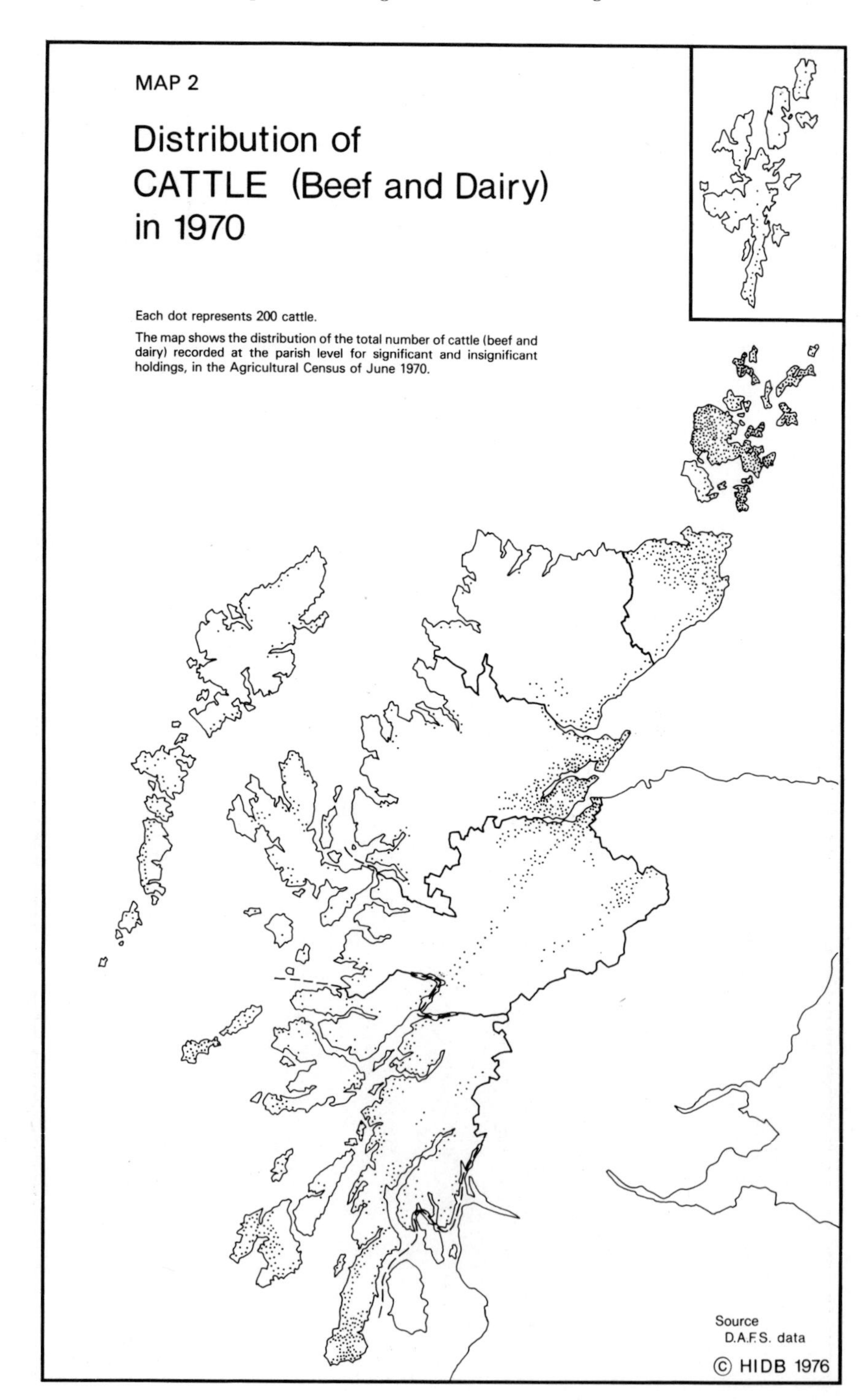
MAP 2
Distribution of
CATTLE (Beef and Dairy)
in 1970
Each dot represents 200 cattle.
The map shows the distribution of the total number of cattle (beef and dairy) recorded at the parish level for significant and insignificant holdings, in the Agricultural Census of June 1970.
Source
D.A.F.S. data
© HIDB 1976

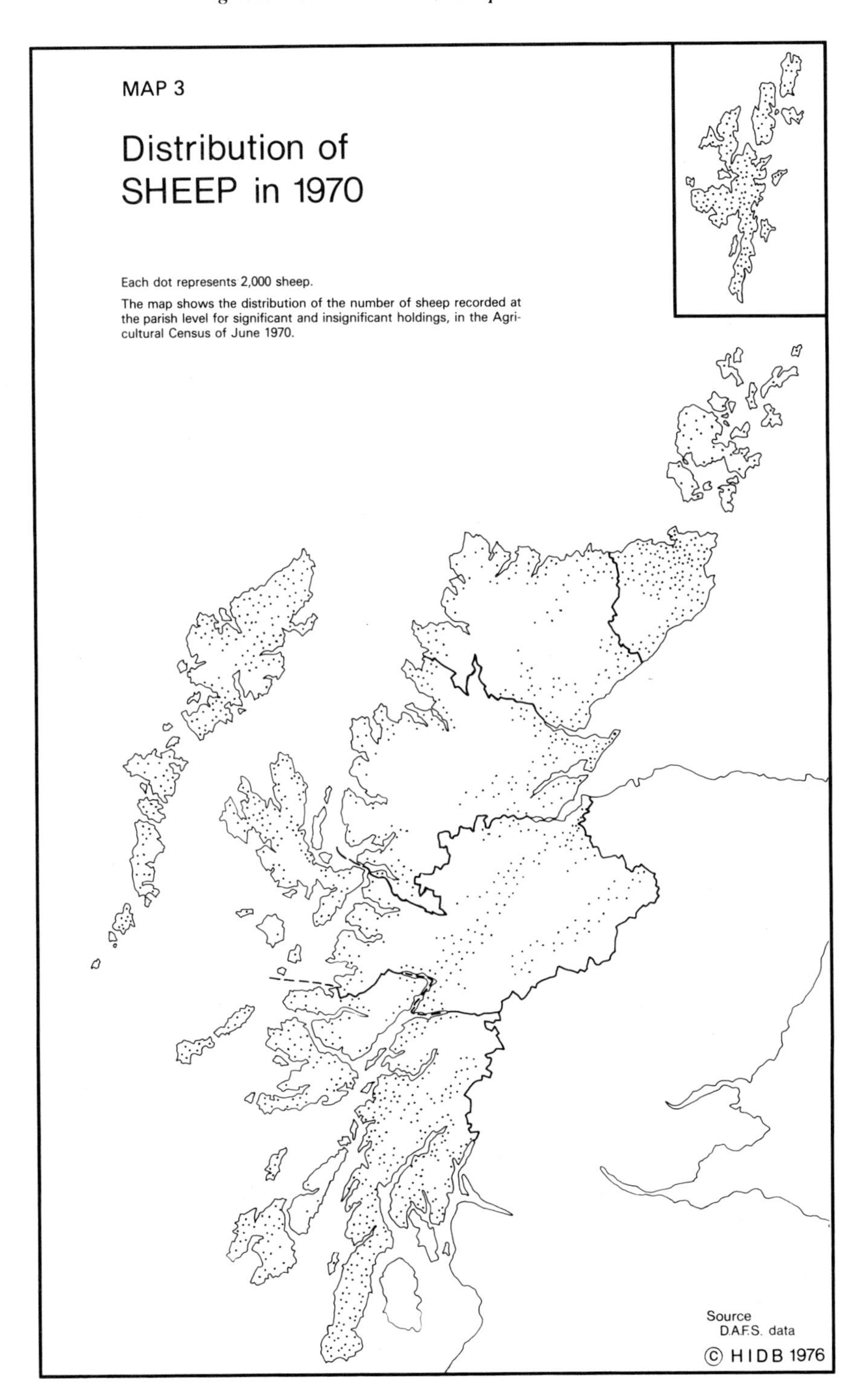
MAP 3
Distribution of SHEEP in 1970
Each dot represents 2,000 sheep.
The map shows the distribution of the number of sheep recorded at the parish level for significant and insignificant holdings, in the Agricultural Census of June 1970.
Source
D.A.F.S. data
© H I D B 1976

Table 1-11 supplements this picture through the use of intensity indices for manpower requirements, hill cows and ewes. By ranking the areas according to their ratio of ewes to labour a close relationship is revealed between this ranking and that based on their ratios of land to labour and hill cows to labour. The more intensive are manpower requirements relative to land, the higher the ratio of cows to manpower and the lower the ratio of ewes to manpower. One exception to a very regular picture is Shetland where an 'average' man/land ratio is associated with a much greater dependence on sheep than cattle. The Moray Firth parishes, with their arable and livestock feeding enterprises show up with relatively low hill cow and ewe ratios.

Table 1-11. Indices of manpower/land and livestock/manpower intensities by County[a] 1970

	Manpower[b] *Index*	*Hill Cow*[b] *Index*	*Ewe*[b] *Index*
Orkney	616	138	16
Moray Firth Parishes[a]	252	68	28
Caithness	244	121	68
Argyll	100	105	142
Inverness[a]	60	113	153
Sutherland	33	86	174
Ross & Cromarty[a]	31	62	191
Shetland	98	47	221
All crofting counties	100	100	100

a The Moray Firth parishes are listed separately and the figures for Inverness and Ross and Cromarty exclude them.

b These indices are constructed as follows: The Manpower Index expresses the corresponding entry in column 2 of Table 1.10 as a percentage of the entry in column 1 of that table; the Hill Cow Index expresses column 3 entries in Table 1.10 as a percentage of column 2 entries and the Ewe Index expresses column 4 entries also as a percentage of column 2 entries.

From this breakdown of the regional data the 'Highland farm' may be provisionally divided into two broad sectors each contributing about half of the output. One sector, located mainly in Orkney, north-east Caithness, the Moray Firth and parts of Argyll, consists of fairly intensive commercial farms with the emphasis on cattle rather than sheep (and including, as we have seen, important intensive and arable enterprises). The other sector extends over most of the islands and large areas of the mainland; it includes almost all the crofts and much of the sheep farming and is likely to include most of the more intractable agricultural 'problems'.

Farm Structure

Such a geographical picture is only one aspect of the story, however; all farms of a particular size and type are not found within well-defined localities and further analyses of the data are needed to bring out other structural features of Highland agriculture. The first point to make is that, out of a total of 22,937 agricultural holdings in the Highlands in 1970, 10,230 were classified as 'insignificant' in that their standard man-day requirement was less than 26 SMDs.[21] Of these, 7,556 were crofts, accounting for nearly half the total number of croft holdings, which was 15,540 in 1970.

Virtually all (probably over 97 per cent) of Highland agricultural production comes from the 12,707 significant holdings. As most of the available data refer to these units we shall, from now on, equate them with the 'Highland farm'; the slight distortions involved will not affect the main conclusions although it may be necessary to recall the existence of the excluded holdings for certain purposes. For completeness, Table 1-12 summarises the county acreage data on such excluded holdings; despite their current 'insignificance' from the viewpoint of farm production, the total acreage covered by them cannot be ignored in the long run.

Table 1-12. Number and Acreage of 'Insignificant' Holdings in the Crofting Counties: 1970

County	*Number of 'insignificant' holdings*	*Total allocated acreage*[a]	*Crops and Grass Acreage*
Argyll	788	27,615	4,873
Caithness	443	20,742	3,402
Inverness	2,794	282,935	19,187
Orkney	617	8,468	5,830
Ross and Cromarty	3,696	160,824	16,232
Sutherland	865	5,933	4,628
Shetland	1,027	18,703	3,828
	10,230	641,221	57,980

Note:
a Excluding common grazings associated with 'insignificant' crofts. These cannot be estimated with any accuracy but could raise the acreage to 800,000 or even higher.

Source: Agricultural Statistics.

Taking the region as a whole, the 12,707 significant holdings covered a total acreage of 6,338,100[22] in 1970,[23] including a crops and grass acreage

21 In more recent years the lower limit of 40 SMDs has been used.

22 Excluding common grazing which for *all* holdings totalled 1,200,000 acres.

23 1970 is used in this analysis because it is the most recent year for which certain structural data are available. There have been no big changes since then.

of 541,817. 6,991 holdings had less than 100 standard man-day requirements, a further 2,594 had between 100 and 250 SMDs and only 3,122 had more than 250 SMDs. This implies that only one quarter of all significant holdings qualified (in terms of SMDs) as 'full-time' holdings.

The distribution of SMDs over these various size groups is shown in Table 1-13. The 'full-time units' which make up about 25 per cent of the total number of significant holdings accounted for 75 per cent of SMDs, a further 20 per cent of holdings (with 100-250 SMDs) accounted for 13 per cent and the remaining small units (26-100 SMDs) while representing 55 per cent of the significant holdings accounted for only 12 per cent of SMDs.

A geographical breakdown of these data is also made in Table 1-13 with Moray Firth parishes treated separately. The apparently dual nature of the Highland agricultural economy is again suggested. The Moray Firth parishes, Argyll, Orkney and Caithness emerge as areas where about half the significant holdings are full-time farms accounting for between 73 and 90 per cent of the labour requirements (a rough proxy for output) of these areas. Shetland and the remaining part of Ross and Cromarty show up with a very different structure, roughly half the SMDs being on small units (with under 100 SMDs) which account for about 80 per cent of all significant holdings. Sutherland and Inverness (excluding the Moray Firth parishes) show a remarkably similar structure to each other but are not quite so extreme as Shetland and Ross-shire.

Table 1-13. Frequency Distribution of Standard Man-Days, by size groups, on all significant holdings, 1970

	26-100 SMD's		*100-250 SMD's*		*over 250 SMD's*	
	holdings %	*SMD's* %	*holdings* %	*SMD's* %	*holdings* %	*SMD's* %
All crofting counties	55	12	20	13	25	75
Moray Firth Parishes	29	3	21	7	50	90
Argyll	31	4	19	7	50	89
Caithness	35	6	24	13	41	81
Orkney	27	5	25	22	48	73
Sutherland	66	20	20	18	14	62
Inverness (excluding Moray Firth parishes)	66	22	20	19	14	59
Ross and Cromarty (excluding Moray Firth parishes)	86	47	9	16	5	37
Shetland	78	46	18	29	4	25

Source: Based on data supplied by DAFS.

With full-time farms accounting for around 75 per cent of Highland farm output, the structure and location of this sector of the region's agriculture is of particular interest. As Table 1-14 shows, the Highlands' 3,122 full-time farms represented in 1970 about one-seventh of all full-time farms in

Scotland and in manpower requirements their average size was about 70 per cent of the Scottish average. Nearly 79 per cent of Highland full-time farms were in Orkney, Caithness, Argyll and the Moray Firth parishes and in the last area the average size of farm was quite close to the Scottish average.

Table 1-14. Number and average size (in SMDs) of full-time holdings, by county,[a] 1970

	Number of full-time holdings	*Average size SMD's*
Scotland	22,268	990
All crofting counties	3,122	706
of which —		
Moray Firth parishes	604	919
Argyll	764	798
Caithness	457	603
Orkney	634	540
Ross and Cromarty[a]	93	656
Inverness[a]	382	717
Sutherland	122	787
Shetland	66	515

Note: a excluding Moray Firth parishes.
Source: Based on data supplied by DAFS.

If we define 'big' farms as those with over 1,000 standard man-days we find that this group, although numbering only 628 farms, accounted for nearly half the labour requirements of all full-time farms (or about one-third of all SMDs) in the Highlands and Islands. Highland agriculture certainly includes a much higher proportion of part- and spare-time holdings and its full-time farms are also smaller than in Scotland as a whole but there is nevertheless the same tendency as elsewhere for a relatively small number of larger farms to produce a very high proportion of the output. To put it more starkly, about one-third of Highland agricultural output probably comes from 628 farms representing 5 per cent of all 'significant' holdings and less than 3 per cent of the total of 23,000 agricultural holdings of all kinds. The geographical distribution of these larger farms is shown in Table 1-15 and reveals that the proportion of such farms in Orkney, Caithness, the Moray Firth and Argyll (80 per cent) is almost exactly the same as the proportion of all full-time farms in these areas (79 per cent).

The concentration of labour requirements on larger farms implies that livestock will show a similar distribution. Cattle numbers are more densely concentrated than sheep, however; one-third of all beef cows are on only 464 farms, whereas 827 of the farms with the largest ewe flocks are needed to account for one-third of all ewes. This is consistent with the general picture given by the dot maps earlier in this section.

Table 1-15. Geographical distribution of 628 largest farms in the Highlands and Islands (measured in SMDs) in 1970

Size groups (in SMD's)	*Moray Firth Parishes*	*Argyll*	*Caithness*	*Orkney*	*Inverness*	*Ross and Cromarty*	*Sutherland*	*Shetland*	*All Crofting Counties*
1,000-1,200	37	59	30	19	29	4	9	1	188
1,200-1,500	44	59	17	21	17	4	11	—	173
1,500-1,800	26	27	16	10	12	—	5	1	97
1,800-3,000	52	26	19	10	12	3	10	—	132
over 3,000	19	11	1	—	5	1	—	1	38
TOTAL	178	182	83	60	75	12	35	3	628

Source: Based on data supplied by DAFS.

Crofting structure

So far, only passing reference has been made to the existence of croft holdings as distinct from other kinds of agricultural holdings. This has been deliberate for the concern of this chapter has been with economic measures of agricultural production, incomes and structure rather than with forms of land tenure. Nevertheless, crofts[24] are recognised as special holdings for policy purposes and their location and structural features are obviously relevant to a descriptive account of Highland agriculture. The paragraphs which follow, it should be emphasised, are designed to supplement our earlier analysis and not to provide a comprehensive picture of 'crofting' which would have to deal with much more than agricultural production.

As mentioned before, out of a total of 15,540 croft holdings in 1970,[25] only 7,984 were classified as 'significant' in the sense that their standard man-day requirement was at least 26 days a year. Taking the average ratio of 'significant' to 'insignificant' croft holdings as 1:1 the county ratios in Table 1-16 show that the main variations from the norm are in Caithness and Orkney (where the ratio favours the significant holdings) and in Ross and Cromarty where 'insignificant' croft holdings are predominant.

The total (allocated) acreage returned for these 'insignificant' croft holdings was 115,951 in 1970 (out of a total of 641,221 acres for all insignificant holdings) but to this should be added an (unknown) proportion of the common grazings. Improving the use of this land in the future must be kept in mind as one long-term policy objective but at present these 7,556 crofts probably contribute little more than one per cent to Highland agricultural production. The rest of our analysis will concentrate on the other 7,984 crofts requiring at least 26 standard man-days. As before, we shall begin by treating this sector as a whole, discussing the 'Highland croft' as we did the 'Highland farm' (which, of course, included crofts).

The contribution of the Highland croft to the agricultural output of the region is difficult to estimate. According to labour requirements measured in SMDs the proportion would be 28 per cent, but this can only be a rough guide since the relative technical productivity and relative value of the products would probably lead to a significant downward adjustment. Crofts accounted for 33 per cent of the ewes and 27 per cent of the hill cows in the region in that year, so their contribution in these sectors is substantial. However, the statistics for crofts cover any census unit with crofting land and include some with substantial areas of non-crofting land. As a very rough estimate, therefore, the Highland croft may contribute between 20

24 Legally a croft is now a holding which is recognised as such by the Crofters Commission. A formal description is given in Appendix 1B.

25 There were 18,149 crofts entered in the Crofters Commission register at 31 December 1974, but only an estimated 14,162 were classified as 'working units' corresponding to the figure for 'croft holdings' used above. The difference is accounted for by real and 'paper' amalgamations between 1970 and 1974.

Table 1-16. Number of all Holdings and 'Significant' and 'Insignificant' croft holdings by counties, 1970

County	*Column 1 No. of all 'significant' holdings*	*Column 2 No. of 'significant' croft holdings*	*Column 3 Col. 2 as a percentage of col 1 %*	*Column 4 No. of 'insignificant' croft holdings*	*Ratio of col 2: col 4*
Argyll	1,536	530	35	416	5:4
Caithness	1,125	585	52	196	3:1
Inverness	3,215	2,455	76	2,301	1:1
Orkney	1,677	404	24	90	4:1
Ross and Cromarty	2,758	1,996	72	3,028	2:3
Sutherland	897	747	83	764	1:1
Shetland	1,489	1,258	84	761	13:8
All crofting counties	12,707	7,984	63	7,556	1:1

Source: Based on data supplied by DAFS.

Table 1-17. Distribution of Land, Manpower requirements, Cattle and Sheep on 'Significant' Croft Holdings, by county,[a] 1970

County	*Percentage of crofts*	*Percentage of total acreage*[b]	*Percentage of of standard man-days*	*Percentage of hill cows*	*Percentage of ewes*
Argyll	7	13	9	12	9
Caithness	7	11	14	16	8
Inverness	31	37	28	34	28
Orkney	5	5	9	13	1
Ross and Cromarty	25	14	20	13	21
Shetland	16	11	12	5	22
Sutherland	9	9	8	7	12
Totals for all crofting counties	7,984 croft holdings	646,889 acres	845,823 SMD's	30,568 hill cows	372,991 ewes

Notes:

a In this case it was not considered necessary to separate the Moray Firth parishes as was done in earlier tables.

b Excluding common grazings; these cannot readily be allocated.

Source: Based on data supplied by DAFS.

Table 1-18. Distribution of Standard Man-Days on 'Significant' Croft Holdings by Main Size Groups, 1970

Size Groups (by SMD's)	*No. of Crofts*	*% of Crofts*	*% of SMD's*
		%	%
26-50	3,129	39.2	13.6
50-100	2,610	32.7	21.6
100-250	1,624	20.4	29.8
Over 250	621	7.7	35.0
TOTAL	7,984	100.0	100.0

Source: Based on data supplied by DAFS.

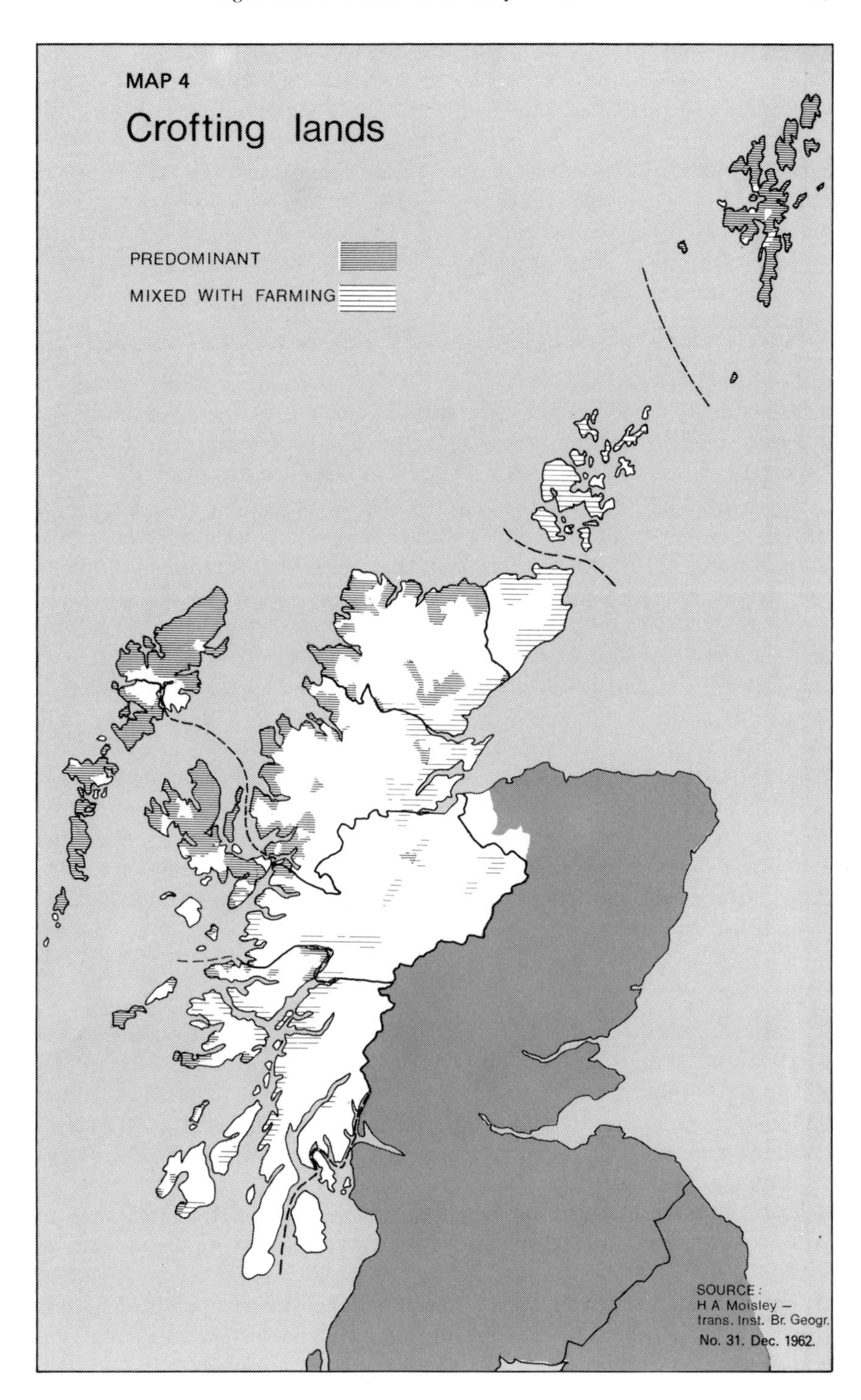
MAP 4
Crofting lands
PREDOMINANT
MIXED WITH FARMING
SOURCE:
H A Moisley –
trans. Inst. Br. Geogr.
No. 31. Dec. 1962.

and 25 per cent of Highland agricultural production. This would put the value of its gross output in 1971-72 at about £8 million and of net output (and therefore agricultural income) at somewhere around £4 million. This implies in turn an average net income from agriculture of occupiers of *significant* crofts (ie half of all crofts) of £400 to £500 in 1971-72, but this is obviously a very approximate figure. What is important is to note that croft output is still a substantial element of Highland agriculture and that, on many crofts which remain in agricultural production, the income from farming, while inadequate as a sole source of income, is nevertheless important.

The geographical distribution of crofts within the Highlands and Islands is shown in Map 4 and requires little additional comment. Crofting agriculture is clearly more important in the islands and along the western seaboard. On a county basis, Inverness, Ross-shire and Shetland emerge as the most important, accounting for over 70 per cent of all croft holdings.

An analysis of the size structure of the significant croft holdings (by SMDs) shows that of the total of 7,984 only 621 or 7.7 per cent were classed as 'full-time', i.e. with over 250 standard man-day requirements, and a further 1,624 or 20.4 per cent had been 100 and 250 SMDs (Table 1-18). The share of SMDs in the various size groups is indicated in the same table and suggests that about 65 per cent of the output of the Highland croft came from units which were not classed as 'full-time' (in terms of SMDs). It seems that about 4,000 crofts which were not full-time required more than one day's labour a week and accounted for about half the Highland croft's total output (and therefore around 10 per cent of Highland agricultural output). Further detailed analysis is probably unnecessary; the main and obvious point is that crofts provide a high proportion of the part-time and spare-time holdings in the Highlands and that, on a substantial minority, agriculture is still important. About 600 crofts are roughly equivalent to small full-time farms.

Conclusions

This chapter has attempted to set out in a systematic way the available data on Highland agricultural production, its value, geographical distribution and structural pattern. The purpose has not only been to provide factual information, but also to highlight those economic features of Highland farming which could be relevant to a discussion of policies likely to assist its development in a changing economy.

Agriculture is still substantially more important to the Highlands than to Scotland as a whole but its economic role has been declining just as rapidly as elsewhere. More importantly, perhaps, over the last 100 years Highland farming has been contributing a diminishing share of Scottish agricultural output and it is only in recent years that there have been signs that the share may be stabilising (at close to 10 per cent). Insofar as it has been legitimate to treat the Highland economy as a special case requiring special policy measures (in order, primarily, to maintain, if not enlarge, settled communities in existing populated areas) so there have been grounds for considering a regional approach, backed up by regional measures, for Highland agriculture.

In determining the content of such a regional agricultural policy, certain features of the farm economy are important. The continuing and growing dominance of sheep and beef cattle rearing within the Highlands suggests that these are among the main enterprises which should be encouraged to become more efficient and technically advanced. If national policy does not sufficiently protect this kind of farming from short-term market fluctuations then regional measures should be adopted which could do so in line with more long-term economic and social objectives.

Differences within Highland agriculture suggest that various policy approaches are likely to be required. Our analysis has shown that at least two 'sectors' exist — the more intensive commercial farming sector concentrated in Orkney, Caithness, the Moray Firth and parts of Argyll, and the more extensive (and, in some areas, part-time) agriculture that exists in other parts. Croft holdings are still important in many areas and present a special agricultural problem (as distinct from a land tenure problem). Measures designed to help the farmers of Caithness or southern Argyll to reach a higher level of income and economic efficiency are not likely to be directly applicable to island crofters trying to make a substantial part (but not necessarily all) of their livelihood from the land.

Insofar as one can generalise about Highland agriculture as a whole, the relatively smaller units (measured in SMD's) and the relatively lower incomes of occupiers are obvious points of difference with the rest of Scotland. Attempts to raise income per head by a drastic reduction in the number of occupiers would accentuate the regional problem as manifested in rural areas. The main objective must be to search for measures which will help to remove some of the obstacles preventing producers (of all kinds) from making better use of the land and other resources presently available in the Highlands and thus to raise their output and income. From the evidence of this chapter, some of these obstacles are likely to be of a financial kind (such as a credit shortage resulting from low incomes) but others could be related more closely to structural and institutional issues — such as the tenure, ownership and control of land. Special difficulties are likely to arise from the presence of many part-time units and the substantial areas of land linked to holdings where individual output is classed as 'insignificant'.

APPENDIX 1A

"Agricultural Employment and Occupied Population"[a]

This appendix relates to Tables 1-1 and 1-2 and is as much a tale of caution as of explanation. Within the United Kingdom the comparison of successive censuses can be a risky venture. Basic spatial units for data collection change, the content of questions varies and definitions and subdivisions relating to particular socio-economic variables are liable to alter. When the comparison is extended to a set of censuses which embrace a century of dynamic social and economic change then the derivation of all but the simplest time series is hazardous. In this particular instance variations in the census concept of agricultural employment and employment in general make analysis specially difficult.

To minimise the problems of time series comparisons with respect to the percentages used in the tables the following steps were taken. The Highlands were consistently defined as the seven crofting counties at each census date. For each census, subdivisions relating to the agricultural sector were examined and subsectors which did not obviously refer to direct agricultural employment were subtracted; in 1871, for instance, land proprietors, woodsmen and estate gardeners were abstracted. In 1911 similar omissions were made and in 1921 subsectors such as foresters, labourers in woods and forests, land drainers, estate gardeners etc. were excluded. Consistency of treatment for Scottish and Highland data was the aim. One group — that of employed dependents — presented special difficulty as redefinitions of this group have tended to become more restrictive and thus to exaggerate the extent of any decline. If, however, it is accepted that the ratio of (employed) dependents to others occupied in agriculture has not varied greatly between the Highlands and Scotland as a whole then we can be more confident about estimates of the declining share of Highland farming in the Scottish agricultural population. We cannot, however, make specific comparisons of absolute percentages for successive years.

a Prepared by Duncan Maclennan, Department of Social and Economic Research, University of Glasgow

APPENDIX 1B
Definition of a Croft[a]

In the Crofters (Scotland) Act 1955 a croft was defined as any holding in the seven crofting counties which:—

1. is situated in a designated crofting parish (a parish in which in 1886 or the preceding 80 years there were holdings comprising arable land and pasturage held in common) and in which there were tenants in 1886 who were resident on their holdings and paying less than £30/year rent. The tenant of such a unit and his heirs and legatees were crofters and if the tenancy continued until 1955 this was a croft; (Crofters Holdings (Scotland) Act 1886)
2. (from 1911) was less than 50 acres or had a rent of less than £50, whose tenant was resident within two miles of the holding and who personally or whose family cultivated the holding and which was an agricultural holding within the meaning of the Agricultural Holdings Acts. The tenant of such a unit and his heirs and legatees were small landholders or statutory small tenants and if the tenancy continued until 1955 this was a croft: (Small Landholders (Scotland) Act 1911)
3. (under the Crofters (Scotland) Act 1961) has less than 75 acres *or* a rent of less than £50 and the landlord and tenant apply to the Secretary of State for a direction that it is a croft and the Secretary of State agrees;
4. is non-crofting land let to an existing crofter and the resultant holding is less than 75 acres or the rent is less than £50, and both landlord and crofter agree that it should be crofting land; or
5. is non-crofting land let to a crofter and the resultant holding is more than 75 acres and the rent is more than £50, and the landlord, crofter and the Secretary of State agree that it should be crofting land.

a We are indebted to S C C Kennedy for guiding us to this rather complex definition.

CHAPTER 2

Rural Land Use, Ownership and Control

Present Land Use

Table 2-1 summarises the existing pattern of land use in the Highlands, although difficulties of estimation affect the reliability of some of the figures.[1]

Table 2-1. Land Use in the Highlands and Islands, circa 1969

Rough Grazings, including deer forest (1969)[a]	7,600,130 acres
Crops and grass (1969)[a]	597,834 acres
Forestry Commission, area planted (1969)[b]	349,672 acres
Private Forestry (Estimate, 1969)[c]	140,000 acres
Unproductive and Scrub (Estimate)[d]	100,000 acres
Built-up areas (Approx)[e]	40,000 acres
Unaccounted for	165,164 acres
Total area	8,992,800 acres

Notes on Sources and Estimates

a DAFS. Agricultural Statistics 1969.

b Source: Forestry Commission.

c Based on the figure given in the Report on Land Use in the Highlands and Islands of 120,500 acres planted on private estates plus an estimated planting rate of approximately 3,000 acres per annum thereafter. HMSO (1964).

d Based on a figure given in the Report of the Select Committee on Scottish Affairs 1971-72, Vol III p 269 adjusted for felled woodlands which will be included in the forestry acreages given above. The summary sheets for the 1973 June Census of Agriculture show 11,382 acres of roads, yards and buildings and 40,687 acres of woodlands on farms in the Crofting Counties (excluding 'insignificant' holdings).

e Select Committee Report, Vol III p 269. The area of Urban Land in Scotland (including roads and railways) was estimated at 470,000 acres in 1950/51 or 92 acres per 1,000 population (Best & Coppock (1962)). On a *per capita* basis this would give an urban land area of some 26,000 acres in the Highlands and Islands. However, the acreage *per capita* is likely to be higher than for Scotland, one reason being the higher mileage of road *per capita*.

1 For example, the absence of accurate up-to-date information on private forestry, the lack of reliable information on 'urban' land (including roads), the considerable overlap between different uses, particularly deer and other sporting uses, with agriculture and, to some extent, forestry, and the probability that some of the land classified as rough grazing is not in fact being used (See also Chapter 1, page 21).

The very high proportion of rough grazings in the Highlands and Islands (84 per cent) and correspondingly low proportion of crops and grass (< 7 per cent) as compared with Scotland as a whole (64 per cent and >22 per cent respectively)[2] indicate the environmental limitations of the region. Whilst the stock carrying capacity of the rough grazings can be considerable during the summer months, the limited capacity to grow and conserve winter keep presents a fundamental problem to livestock farming over much of the region. As a consequence of this, an increase in the quantity and quality of winter fodder grown, and allied attempts to provide areas of improved grazing in the spring and autumn, should be major objectives of any agricultural development policy for the Highlands.

The predominance of agriculture in primary land use, reflected in Table 2-1, is also shown in Table 2-2 which compares the output from various land using activities in 1972.[3] Caution must be exercised in using these figures since the estimates of gross output from the different uses are not

Table 2-2. Estimated Gross Output of Primary Land Uses — Highlands and Islands, 1971/2

	Highlands & Islands		**Scotland**	
	£ millions	%	*£ millions*	%
Agriculture[a]	37.5	91.0	340.1	97.6
Forestry[b]	2.8	6.8	7.5	2.1
Deer,[c] carcase meat	0.5	1.9	0.5	0.2
imputed rents	0.3		0.3	
Grouse,[d] as game	0.02	0.3	0.1	0.1
imputed rents	0.06		0.3	
Other game[e]	<0.05		<0.1	
Total, all primary uses	41.2	100%	348.8	100%

Notes:

a The estimate of agricultural output includes an estimate of £412,000 for 'other livestock', which are said to include rabbits and game. See Table 1-3 note c. Although this looks rather low, there may therefore be an element of double counting in the above table.

b 1971/2. Production of 452,000 m^3 in the HIDB area. 1.2 million m^3 in Scotland. Average price £2.74 m^3 as standing timber plus £3.50 per m^3 for felling and extraction to give roadside values. Excludes value of growth of standing timber — probably worth some £6 million in 1973 in the Crofting Counties. During 1973 timber prices rose substantially.

c Based on Red Deer Commission Annual Report 1972. See text for details.

d Based on Tivy, in Tivy (ed) 1973, and information within the HIDB regarding rents and bird prices. See also text.

e Estimated by Board Staff.

2 These percentages are from Annex 1 in the Board's evidence to the Select Committee on Scottish Affairs, Session 1971-72, Land Resource Use in Scotland Volume III, HMSO (1972).

3 This is also shown by the employment figures given in Chapter 3.

strictly comparable, and the estimates for grouse and other game are speculative, there being no recent reliable estimates of the production involved.[4]

Agricultural Land Use

The pattern of agricultural land use in the Highlands and Islands reflects the restricted choice of enterprises over most of the area due to the environmental factors discussed below, and the predominance of extensive livestock enterprises referred to in the previous chapter. Isolation, relative poverty and structural influences have also meant that subsistence cropping has had an important — if declining — role to play by comparison with the rest of the country. These two principal factors have influenced agricultural land use in the region for a period far longer than the century or so which is recorded by reasonably reliable and comprehensive statistics. As Table 2-3 shows, the total area of arable land has declined slightly over the past 100 years, while the area devoted to crops other than grass has shown a marked decline — principally because of a steady fall in the acreage of oats, potatoes and turnips. Potatoes and oats were important subsistence crops during the 18th and 19th Centuries, whilst the latter were also used for the payment of rentals and for payment of other services which farmers required.[5] It may be inferred from these figures that the area of cultivated grassland increased over the period, and the figure given for grass cultivated for hay in 1878 of some 78,500 acres for the Crofting Counties[6] may be compared with the figure of 136,380 acres of grass for cutting in 1974.[7] Almost all this increase in conserved grass has occurred in the last 30 years and mainly in Orkney and Caithness.

The changing pattern of agricultural land use in the Highlands is to a large extent a reflection of the changes in Scotland as a whole, where the area of land devoted to arable crops has also declined. The principal difference is that, taking the period as a whole, the area of land under cereals and potatoes has declined much less rapidly in Scotland than in the Highlands.[8] Table 2-4 shows that these declines were to some extent — but not entirely — offset by the rather faster rate of increase in yields of most arable crops in the Crofting Counties, at least in the period since 1907.

4 The HIDB is currently financing a study which will allow much more precise estimates of output, income and employment from this sector. The results of this study should be available during 1976.

5 cf Handley J E, Scottish Farming in the 18th Century (Faber 1953), pp 82 *et seq*. Oats and other commodities were also used for payment *in lieu* of other services which landlords commonly required of their tenantry.

6 Trans. H & A Soc Scot. 1879, p 216.

7 DAFS. June Census 1974. Data exclude insignificant holdings of < 40 SMDs.

8 See also Table 1-4.

Table 2-3. Agricultural Land Use in the Highlands and Islands 1878-1974 ('000 acres)

	1878	*1907*	*1937*	*1958*	*1968*	*1974*
Arable[a]	451.2	467.8	434.0	411.8	420.6	377.1
Permanent Grass[b]	205.6	264.0	227.0	209.1	174.2	148.4
Tillage[c]	303.4	281.7	214.7	186.4	155.3	120.1
of which,						
Wheat	4.6	1.0	2.0	2.1	6.7	3.1
Barley	32.3	27.5	10.6	10.0	36.0	54.9
Oats	161.9	158.5	135.7	112.9	69.6	34.9
Potatoes	34.1	26.1	18.1	12.8	8.4	4.3
Turnips	64.2	63.5	46.5	33.4	18.7	14.2
Cabbage & Kale	0.4	1.2	1.0	2.4	1.3	1.1
Rape	0.4	0.2	0.6	5.6	4.4	3.1

Notes:

a Crops and rotation grass including fallow.

b 7 years +

c Arable less rotation grass and bare fallow.

Source: Agricultural Statistics.

Table 2-4. Long term yield changes in arable crops, Scotland and the Crofting Counties

	1907		*1968*		*% Change 1907-1968*	
	Crofting Counties	*Scotland*	*Crofting Counties*	*Scotland*	*Crofting Counties*	*Scotland*
Wheat (cwt/acre)	18.6	22.0	36.9	33.5	98.4	52.3
Barley (cwt/acre)	14.6	17.2	28.0	28.9	91.8	68.0
Oats (cwt/acre)	11.1	13.8	19.5	22.3	75.7	61.6
Potatoes (tons/acre)	3.7	5.5	7.2[a]	8.7[a]	94.6	58.2
Turnips (tons/acre)	12.2	14.7	17.5	21.9	43.4	49.0
Hay (cwt/acre)	24.1	33.1	34.1	40.8	41.5	23.3

Note: a Av. 1963-67.

Source: Agricultural Statistics.

Data presented in Chapter 1 show that arable farming in the Highlands is now located predominantly in the Moray Firth area, and most of the decline in arable acreage over the long term has probably come from a decline in arable farming in other areas of the region. This probably explains a part of the difference in yield changes described above. For most of the area, however, it is changes in the production from livestock enterprises that are more important indicators of changes in the intensity of agricultural land use.

Estimates of long term changes in livestock populations have been made for the period since 1800 and these show a switch in production from cattle to sheep during the 19th Century, but a greater expansion of cattle than sheep thereafter. By 1974 cattle numbers in the Highlands exceeded the level attained in 1800. Over this period, the character of both cattle and sheep in the region had changed markedly, whilst numbers of other grazing livestock — particularly horses and goats — had declined.[9]

In Scotland, on the other hand, although a similar expansion in sheep numbers took place during the 19th Century, there was no compensatory decline in cattle numbers during this period, and the cattle population has continued to rise up to the present day. Sheep numbers also expanded in the period since 1878, although at a much slower rate. Since the 1950's there has been a small but significant decline in the sheep population.

It is particularly difficult to assess changes in the physical productivity of livestock since 1800. The period from 1800 to 1878 saw profound agrarian change in the Highlands, as elsewhere in Scotland. New breeds of both cattle and sheep were introduced during the Clearances and the output by 1878 was clearly of a different character from that in 1800.[10] Although it is certain that the output of meat and wool from sheep increased over this period,[11] the changes in cattle output are more difficult to gauge.

Highland cattle — predominantly of the type generally described as "Kyleoes" — at the end of the 18th Century were small by present day standards, and stots and heifers destined for fatstock markets were kept in the Highlands for three or four years before being sold to the "Drovers" who took them south to the markets at Falkirk or elsewhere.[12] Accounts of these cattle vary, but they seem to have reached only 3-4 cwt at three to four years of age.[13] It therefore seems unlikely that more than one-fifth of the cattle population in 1800 would be available for sale — or about 70,000 animals at the most. This compares with Haldane's estimate of 60,000 animals sold from the Highlands in 1794, which is, in turn, based on Sir John Sinclair's estimate of revenue from cattle sales.[14] In terms of beef production, this might represent a liveweight of between 10,000 and 14,000

9 Draught oxen were in common use in the Highlands at the time of the First Statistical Account (1790s); indeed they continued to be used in Shetland until the advent of the tractor, although in most other parts of the region horses became the most usual source of power during the 19th Century.

10 There was also a continuing — but unquantifiable — decline in goat numbers over this period, again associated with the Clearances. According to Smout goats were important as dairy and meat animals up to and including the 18th Century. They also provided cash income . . . '100,000 goat and kid skins were sent to London in a single year' from the Highlands at the end of the 17th Century. Smout T C (1969) p 130. See also Clerk D (1881) pp 227-228, and Burt (1754) cited in Smout.

11 Haldane (1951) p 201. References are to the 1968 edition.

12 Haldane (1951) *passim*.

13 MacDonald (1811) and Smith (1798) cited in Haldane (1951) Appendix C.

14 Haldane (1951) p 205.

Table 2-5. Cattle and sheep populations, 1800-1974

	1800	*1878*	*1907*	*1937*	*1958*	*1968*	*1974*[e]
Crofting Counties							
Cattle[a]	356,400	231,824	224,798	198,805	271,137	316,953	399,803
Of which breeding herd[b]	n.a.	90,182	92,506	84,147	116,032	141,217	172,950[f]
Sheep[c]	641,300	2,540,429	2,176,183	2,093,449	2,519,622	2,582,453	2,318,198
Of which breeding ewes[d]	n.a.	n.a.	945,624	973,009	1,138,915	1,200,315	1,041,804
Scotland							
Cattle[a]	1,047,142	1,095,387	1,185,452	1,289,913	1,819,590	2,077,674	2,675,893
Of which breeding herd[b]	n.a.	388,002	438,955	495,290	717,557	833,345	1,013,741
Sheep[c]	2,851,867	7,036,396	7,313,155	7,517.871	7,929,302	7,849,179	7,571,044[g]
Of which breeding ewes[d]	n.a.	n.a.	n.a.	3,285,191	3,313,184	3,389,698	3,134,002[g]

Notes:
a Dairy and Beef Cattle of whatever description.
b Cows or Heifers in Milk or in Calf.
c All Sheep.
d Excludes 'Other sheep 1 year old and over for breeding'.
e Excludes stock on 'insignificant' holdings of <40 SMD's.
f Excludes 'Other cows retained for breeding'.
g There were 217,322 sheep on 'insignificant' holdings in Scotland in 1974, of which 94,447 were ewes for breeding.

Sources: 1800 — Sinclair, Sir John (ed) General Report of the Agricultural State and Political Circumstances of Scotland, 5 vols (1814). Estimated using data from County Reports and the First Statistical Account of Scotland.

1878 — present day. Agricultural Statistics.

tons, which is less than one-third of contemporary estimates.[15] Changes in milk production are much more difficult to gauge, but broadly two factors have been important. First, the decline of the house cow in all parts of the area. Second, the concentration of commercial production structurally among fewer producers and also geographically in Orkney, Caithness and the Moray Firth area. Although dairy cow numbers have remained fairly static over the past twenty years, *Russell*[16] has estimated that milk yields have doubled in this period in the North of Scotland Milk Board area, which includes the Northern Counties from Moray to Orkney.

The ratio of breeding cows to total cattle has increased since 1800 although precise data for the early years are not available. Breeding cows in 1800 probably numbered about 80,000 or somewhat under a quarter of total cattle numbers. By 1878, improvements in breeding and in transportation[17] enabled cattle to be sold economically at younger ages and the proportion of breeding cows had increased to 39 per cent. By 1968 — probably encouraged by the introduction of hill cow subsidies — the proportion was 45 per cent. During the latter part of the 19th Century and early part of this, the nature of cattle production in the Highlands changed rapidly as a result of cheap imports, new knowledge of cattle breeding and feeding and the diminishing relative importance of subsistence production. These changes probably led to quite rapid increases in the physical productivity of cattle, and although numbers had fallen in the Highlands, it seems likely that meat output from cattle increased over this period. Thereafter, the rate of increase in physical meat output in relation to the cattle population, particularly in the western areas, has probably been reduced by the tendency, started by the effects of foreign imports on demand but encouraged by the introduction of hill cow subsidies and the reduction of self sufficiency in winter feed, towards selling stock from many areas at younger ages and lighter weights, although cattle numbers and meat output from the region have both risen.

With sheep, the introduction of 'improved' breeds from the end of the 18th century was directly associated with the growing needs of industrial Britain for meat and wool. Sheep numbers increased dramatically during the 19th Century, but the decline in the practice of keeping wether flocks[18]

15 These suggest that the liveweight of net output from the region today probably exceeds 40,000 tons.

16 Russell, R A. North of Scotland Milk Marketing Board. Personally communicated.

17 Communications — Rail, Road and Sea — in the Highlands improved rapidly between 1800 and 1880 with the opening of rail links to Oban, Kyle, Wick and Thurso; road and bridge improvements by the Commissioners for Highland Roads and Bridges and the expansion of MacBraynes.

18 Wethers, or 'wedders', are castrated male lambs. Wether flocks are still kept in some areas of the Highlands and Islands — eg Lewis. According to Collier, the 'ratio of the price per lb of wedders to that of lambs, which during the 1870s had been 2.47, fell in the 1890s to 2.3 and to 2.02 in the first decade of this century. For the 1920s the ratio was 1.14'. Collier (1953) p 72.

for mutton production and in the practice of off-wintering ewe lambs on lower ground farms outside the hills complicates the analysis of the trends in production and productivity over the last century. The decline in wether production and its replacement by the practice of selling all lambs not kept for breeding purposes during the late summer and autumn can be seen in Table 2-6.

Table 2-6. Sheep under 1 year old as a % of total sheep and breeding ewes at June

	1878	*1907*	*1937*	*1958*	*1968*	*1974*
Sheep <1 yr old as a % of Total Sheep						
Crofting Counties	29.0	35.2	38.2	35.2	37.1	39.6
Scotland	34.0	40.0	43.4	42.7	43.8	46.1
Sheep <1 yr old as a % of Breeding ewes						
Crofting Counties	n.a.	81.1	82.3	77.8	79.7	88.2
Scotland	n.a.	n.a.	99.3	102.3	101.3	111.3

See Notes to Table 2-5.
Sources: As for Table 2-5.

These changes must have led to a proportionate increase in breeding ewe numbers, although this is not apparent after the 1930's. There is, however, little evidence to support that view that the lambing performance of the ewe flock has generally improved over the past 100 years despite improvements in veterinary practices and knowledge of diseases and parasites, and the reasons for this seem to be associated both with the failure to achieve significant improvements in the nutrition of ewes during critical periods and with the decline in the number of shepherds.[19]

Since 1878, and in contrast to cattle, total sheep numbers have at best remained static. Up to the 1930's there was a significant decline in total sheep numbers, and although this trend was reversed by the 1950's by 1974 sheep numbers were only marginally different from those recorded in 1878, even allowing for those on 'insignificant' holdings. According to Collier, the replacement of sheep by deer accounted for 'about 75% of the diminution of Highland sheep stocks since 1880' up to the late 1930's.[20]

19 Darling gives data showing the lambing percentage for the Hebrides which indicates a decline from 82% in 1911 to 63% in 1944. Darling F F (1955) p 237. A similar point has been made recently by Findlay in a study of the parish of Glenelg. He cites records for 1899 for three hirsels in the parish indicating lambing percentages of between 83 and 92 per cent. G D Findlay, personal communication.

20 Collier (1953) p 73. Symon also suggests that the decline in sheep numbers in Argyll, Inverness and Ross from 2,187,000 in 1879 to 1,609,000 in 1914 was associated with clearance of ground for deer forests, but 'Even this reduction . . . did not tell the whole story, since on the low ground of two of these counties many more sheep were being kept towards the end of this period'. Symon J A, Scottish Farming Past and Present, Oliver & Boyd (1959) p 200. For an estimate of the production losses involved, see O'Dell and Walton (1962), Appendix A.

Taking the long term view, although cattle numbers are only now returning to the 1800 levels, there is little doubt that physical productivity in terms of meat output has increased, particularly since the end of the 19th Century. Actual production may have declined as a result of the fall in cattle numbers in the period to 1880, but increased substantially thereafter as a result of the increase in cattle numbers and also productivity changes. With sheep, on the other hand, there is little doubt that physical production increased rapidly in the period to 1880 as a result of both increasing numbers and productivity, but in the period since 1880 numbers have remained static and physical productivity — in terms of lambing percentages at least — has shown no substantial improvement. Given the decline in the practice of keeping wether flocks, it seems likely that the output of both meat and wool has also fallen over this period.

County variations in livestock carry

Overall stocking figures for the Highlands and Islands mask considerable variations at the county level. Numbers of grazing livestock carried — expressed as livestock units — increased significantly between 1878 and 1969 in Orkney and Caithness and, to a lesser extent, in Shetland and Ross and Cromarty. In Sutherland, Inverness and Argyll livestock carry declined over the period. Nevertheless, livestock units carried per arable acre increased in every county, especially in Orkney and Caithness. These trends are no doubt partly due to the decline in the number of horses on farms throughout the region.

Table 2-7. Changes in grazing livestock carried as compared with arable land 1878-1969 Crofting Counties and Scotland

	Livestock Units 1969[a] *(1878 = 100)*	*Arable Area 1969*[b] *(1878 = 100)*	*Livestock Units per Arable Acre*	
			1878	*1969*
Orkney	309	107	0.34	0.97
Shetland	108	62	1.81	3.11
Caithness	224	94	0.37	0.88
Sutherland	98	80	1.57	1.91
Inverness	97	65	1.41	1.66
Argyll	97	87	2.32	3.16
Ross-shire	116	97	0.73	0.87
Highlands and Islands	120	92	1.08	1.40
Scotland	164	91	0.51	0.92

Notes:
a Using a simplified conversion factor of 1 for all cattle and 1/10 for all sheep.
b Crops, rotation grass (grass under 7 years old in recent years) and fallow.
Source: Derived from Agricultural Statistics.

Orkney and Caithness are primarily grass growing counties, and the ratio of arable land to rough and hill grazings is relatively favourable. The improved stocking levels in these counties reflect improvement in grassland utilisation rather than greater dependence on purchased feed. The marked increase in stocking intensity in Shetland reflects the large increase in sheep numbers — from 87,601 in 1878 to 251,702 in 1969 — which more than compensated the decline in cattle numbers in that county over this period. Much of the sheep stock in Shetland was — and is — based on the Shetland breed, noted for its light finishing weights, fine wool and ability to survive under extremely harsh conditions. The apparently high stocking rates partly reflect the use of standard conversion factors for cattle and sheep. Of the other counties, Argyll is perhaps the most interesting since the increase in livestock carried per arable acre reflects a greatly increased dependence on winter feed purchased from outside Argyll, whilst the generally higher stocking levels reflect the somewhat higher quality of hill grazings compared with other counties.

Argyll is also of interest from another standpoint. Overall stocking levels have decreased since 1880, and this is particularly marked in sheep numbers which declined by 256,683, or some 25 per cent, between 1878 and 1969, by far the largest change in any county of the region. Table 2-8 below shows that Argyll had by far the largest increase in forestry acreage of any Highland county over this period and, although more detailed analysis would be required to establish cause and effect, the marked decline in sheep numbers cannot be unrelated to the increase in forestry in the county.

Forestry

One of the major changes in land use over the past century in the Highlands and Islands has been the increase in the acreage under forestry. In 1845 there were some 150,000 acres of forestry in the region. By 1880 this had risen to 261,000 acres and by 1969 close to 500,000 acres. In Scotland as a whole similar trends are apparent, the forestry acreage increasing from just under 600,000 acres in 1845 to 830,000 in 1880 and some 1,300,000 acres in 1969, but the proportion of forestry located in the Highlands and Islands has risen from 25 per cent to 40 per cent between 1845 and 1969.

By 1974 the area under forestry in the region included 437,128 acres in Forestry Commission plantations and an estimated 160,000 acres in Private Forestry. Since 1969 one half of Forestry Commission planting in Scotland has been in this region. As Table 2-9 indicates, this contrasts markedly with the 1950's and 1960's.

The Forestry Commission has about seven years reserve of "plantable" land in the Highlands and Islands — or over 140,000 acres. Within the region, however, some critical areas are down to only two or three years reserve and problems of acquisition have occurred in Mull and the Strath of Kildonan.[21]

21 cf Reports on Mull and the Strath of Kildonan, HIDB. See also Chapter 4.

Table 2-8. Trends in Forestry Acreage, Highlands and Islands and Scotland

	1845[a]	*1880*[b]	*1969*		
	Total	*Total*	*Forestry Commission*[c]	*Private*[d]	*Total*
Argyll	27,977	42,746	150,076	38,000	188,076
Inverness	87,189	162,304	108,846	65,000	173,846
Ross & Cromarty	26,107	43,229	60,538	24,000	84,538
Sutherland	6,520	12,260	27,333	12,000	39,333
Caithness	260	210	2,847	1,000	3,847
Orkney	3	0	32	0	32
Shetland	0	0	0	0	0
Highlands & Islands	148,056	260,749	349,672	140,000	489,672
Scotland	594,679	833,133	826,500	407,188	1,233,688
H & I as % of Scotland	25%	31%	42%	34%	40%

Notes on sources etc

a From Anderson M L (1967) Vol 2 Appendix C. Based on figures given in the New Statistical Account of Scotland (1845).

b Agricultural Returns cited in Hunter, Thomas. Woods, Forests & Estates of Perthshire (Perth: 1883) p 17.

c Area under plantations. Forestry Commission.

d Estimated on the basis of 1963 data given in the Report on Land Use in the Highlands and Islands (1964). See also Table 2-1 above.

Table 2-9. Estimates of Forestry Planting Rates (including Re-stocking) Highlands and Islands and Scotland, Acres per Annum

Year(s) unless otherwise indicated	*Scotland*		*Highlands & Islands*	
	Forestry Commission	*Private*	*Forestry Commission*	*Private*
1950	n.a.	5,400	n.a.	n.a.
1952-55	34,000	n.a.	n.a.	n.a.
1956-60	27,000	15,300 (1959)	10,354 (1959)	4,000 (1959-63)
1961-70	32,000	19,500 (1969)	13,696 (1963)	n.a.
1969-70	38,511	29,000	19,745	n.a.
1970-71	48,804	39,000	25,058	n.a.
1971-72	48,230[a]	40,400[b]	26,240[c]	n.a.
1972-73	43,879	n.a.	24,110	n.a.

Sources: Derived from — Forestry Commission Evidence to Select Committee on Land Use (1963), Land Use in the Highlands & Islands (1964). Annual Reports of the Forestry Commission 1969-70 to 1972-73 inclusive.

Notes:

a Includes 4,830 acres re-stocking.

b Includes 4,130 acres re-stocking and an estimated 348 acres planted without the aid of grants.

c Includes 2,240 acres re-stocking.

Table 2-10. Timber Production: Highlands and Islands and Scotland (Thousand Cubic Metres)

	Forestry Commission		*Private*[b]	
	Scotland	*Highlands & Islands*[a]	*Scotland*	*Highlands & Islands*[c]
1969/70	644	191	96	n.a.
1970/71	619	278	123	n.a.
1971/72	662	273	163	n.a.
1972/73	666	292	193	n.a.

Notes:

a Estimated from Conservancy data excluding forests mainly outwith the Highlands and Islands.

b Excludes felling and thinning on Dedicated estates for which no licence is required. By 31/3/72 the total area of forest under the dedication schemes in Scotland was 209,577 hectares (517,000 acres approx). The figures given above must therefore seriously understate production from the private forestry sector. Estimates prepared by the Department of Forestry, University of Aberdeen, for 1971 suggest that 513,034 cubic metres were thinned or felled from private forests in Scotland (Economic Survey of Private Forestry 1972).

c See text.

Timber production *per se* still accounts for virtually all of the output of forestry in the Highlands and some 292,000 cubic metres were felled or thinned in Forestry Commission forests in 1972/3, compared with the Scottish total of 666,000 cubic metres[22]

22 Derived from Annual Report and Accounts of the Forestry Commission.

Given the absence of reliable data on production from the private forestry sector, it is only possible to make the broadest estimate of the value of timber production. The age of Forestry Commission forests is — on average — lower than those in private woodlands, so that an adjustment on the basis of the acreage in each forestry sector would underestimate production. On the basis of the sample survey of private forests, total production in 1971/72 would be of the order of 1.2 million cubic metres for Scotland as a whole and, on the basis of the regional acreage in private forestry, 452,000 cubic metres in the Highlands. For a rough estimate of gross output at the 'forest gate', felling and extraction costs (including overheads) of about £3.50 per metric ton (roughly equivalent to a cubic metre) have to be added to the average price of £2.74 per cubic metre for standing timber. This gives an approximate Gross Output of £7.5 million for Scotland and £2.8 million for the Highlands and Islands in 1971/72.

These figures exclude the value of the growth of standing timber which is not felled or thinned; production figures of this kind would give an accurate picture of annual output only if the age structure of the forest were even, and this is not the case in Scotland or the Highlands and Islands where planting rates have increased markedly over the past 25 years. Much of our forest has yet to reach the thinning stage. According to Wolfe and Caborn, some 76 per cent of coniferous forests in Britain were less than 30 years old in 1972/3.[23] A similar picture would emerge if complete data were available for Scotland and the Highlands and Islands.

Nevertheless, even counting the value of the growth of standing timber,[24] forestry is clearly of secondary importance — in terms of its gross output taking the Highlands and Islands as a whole — when compared with agriculture. From the regional point of view its significance derives from its apparent ability to provide employment in areas where alternative opportunities are hard to find and also its capacity to generate secondary industry such as the Fort William Pulp Mill.

Deer Forests

Deer forests represent a third important primary use of the land resources of the Highlands and Islands, as they have since the rapid rise in the popularity of stalking during the 19th Century. The number of recorded deer forests increased from nine about 1790 to a peak of 203 in 1912, since when there was a slow decline to 147 in 1957. Similar trends occurred in the

23 Wolfe J N and Caborn J M. 'Some Considerations regarding Forestry Policy in Great Britain'. Forestry Committee of Great Britain, April 1973, Table 42 p 72.

24 Technically speaking changes in 'work in progress' due to volume and cost changes should be added, together with subventions in the nature of production grants. It is not clear to what extent the interest rate subsidies to the Forestry Commission and the fiscal relief and grant aid to the private forestry sector should be included in the value of gross output, but data shortages preclude this in any event.

official acreage of deer forests, which reached a peak of just over 3½ million acres in 1912 and declined to some 2¼ million acres by 1957. It is however difficult to describe the area of deer forest exactly. An estimated 5¾ million acres of land in the Highlands and Islands are reckoned to be used by red deer, and deer have been counted by the Red Deer Commission in some 3.6 million acres.[25] Part of this area is also used by other stock, mainly sheep. In 1957 some 94,000 sheep and 1,800 cattle were carried on recorded deer forests.[26] Much of the area of true deer forest lies above 1,000 feet, although access to lower ground is important for the survival of red deer during harsh weather. Of the 2¾ million acres in deer forest in 1957, probably about 2 million acres lay above the 1,000 feet contour, the area in deer forests below that level having been eroded largely by the expansion of forestry.[27] Conflict with forestry and farming interests was among the more important reasons for the establishment, in 1959, of the Red Deer Commission, which has both conservation and control powers.

The capacity of red deer to utilise poor hill and mountain grazings is related to the mobility of the deer which enables them to move rapidly from low to high ground and vice-versa as weather conditions change, and to their biological efficiency in converting plant material. Nevertheless, the productivity of red deer in the wild is low. Out of a red deer population in the Highlands estimated at 131,500, some 22,000 were culled in 1972/3. The average calving rate, calculated on the estimated number of mature hinds, is roughly 30 per cent. This compares with calving rates of over 90 per cent achieved by the experimental deer farm at Glensaugh run under the direction of the Rowett Research Institute and the Hill Farming Research organisation.[28] The low productivity in the wild is probably due to three main factors — poor culling achievement, nutritional constraints, and conception failures.

According to Mather, the annual output is equivalent to about 1lb of meat per acre at the high end of the range of productive rates, falling to a few ounces on marginal ground.[29] Overall the cull of red deer is worth about £0.5 million at 1972 prices in terms of venison production, and stalking rentals probably amount to roughly £0.3 million in the Highlands and Islands, assuming rentals of £25 per stag in 1972.[30] This is equivalent to about 14 pence per acre calculated on the total area of land used by red deer, or about 35 pence per acre of the recorded area of deer forest.

25 Select Committee Report on Land Use, Vol III p 269.

26 Land Use in the Highlands and Islands (1964) p 78.

27 The Deer Forest Committee of 1922 recorded 2.22 million acres of deer forest above 1,000 feet and 1.39 million acres below 1,000 feet. Report of the Departmental Committee on Deer Forests, 1922.

28 Cunningham, Blaxter, *et al* (1974).

29 Mather A. Appendix to the Annual Report of the Red Deer Commission for 1972.

30 Average prices of £25 for stags and £13 for hinds were cited by Mather. *loc cit.*

Table 2-11. Area of Deer Forests, Scotland[a]

Date	*Forests (No)*	*Acres*	*Source*
1790	9	n.a.	Old Statistical Account
1838	45	n.a.	Scrope
1883	99	1,975,209	Napier Commission
1896	120	2,500,000	Augustus Grimble (incomplete)
1912	203	3,584,916	Deer Forests Committee
1920	189	3,432,385	Deer Forests Committee
1938	194	3,349,131	DAFS
1948	196	3,187,686	DAFS
1957	147	2,233,656	Land Use in the Highlands & Islands

Note:
a Over 90 per cent of Scottish Deer Forest lies within the Highlands and Islands.

Sources: 1790-1948 cited in *Darling* F, West Highland Survey (1955)
1957. Land Use in the Highlands and Islands (1964).

Table 2-12. Area used by Red Deer in Highlands and Islands

Area used by Red Deer in HIDB area	5,750,000 acres
Area in which deer have been counted	3,630,000 acres
Number of deer in counted area	103,500
Estimated number of deer in uncounted area	28,050
Estimated number of deer in HIDB area	131,500
Deer population per 100 acres of total area used	2.06

Source: Derived from Red Deer Commission Data cited in Select Committee Report Vol III p 269.

Table 2-13. Red Deer Purchases, Scotland[a]

	Purchases by Dealers[b]		
	Stags	*Hinds*	*Total*
1970	11,518	12,312	23,830
1971	10,800	11,267	22,067
1972	11,448	11,494	22,942
1973	12,614	12,168	24,782

Notes:
a Of the 1973 total, about 22,000 would be from the Highlands and Islands.
b An unknown — but significant — number of deer, for one reason or another, do not reach dealers.

Source: Red Deer Commission Annual Reports 1970, 1971, 1972 and 1973 (HMSO).

Grouse Moors

Grouse occur over most of the region at summer densities varying from one brace to two acres, or even less, in the more productive heather moors in the east of the region to fewer than one brace to five acres in the wetter areas of the west, where heather tends to be rarer and its management generally poor. Grouse moors in Scotland cover about three million acres, and correspond closely to the area delineated as heather moorland in the regional vegetation maps; about one-third of this area is in the Highlands and Islands, mainly in Inverness-shire, Ross-shire, and Sutherland, and predominantly towards the east of these counties. Grouse occur outwith the area formally described as grouse moor, but numbers are small.

Summer densities average about one brace over six acres of moor in Scotland overall and somewhat less in the Highlands — probably in the region of one brace to ten acres. Since it is reckoned that some 20 per cent of stock — on average — will be shot, the average 'bag' for Scotland may be estimated at 100,000 brace, whilst that for the Highlands and Islands may be reckoned at about 20,000 brace.[31]

Grouse moors were more productive at the beginning of the century than they are today. MacLean's evidence relating to the sporting estates belonging to the Duke of Sutherland gives a total bag estimated at 18,667 brace of grouse (circa 1900) over 45 shoots in Sutherland alone.[32] In the six sporting estates of the Strath of Kildonan, covering in all about 125,000 acres, the bag was 5,200 brace according to this evidence. By comparison, the same estates produced an annual average of 1,813 brace between 1959 and 1969, and the best of those years produced only 2,976 brace.[33] The reason for this probably lies in the decline in the extent and standard of moor management over much of the area, but particularly in the wetter parts. Since moor management for grouse can — if properly executed — improve the productivity for other stock, particularly sheep, this has no doubt had its effect on the performance of sheep in these areas.[34] Management problems have also led to an increase in predators in some areas.

Grouse output comprises actual and imputed rental and the value of the birds as game. Rentals of £30/gun day over a shoot producing 10 brace per

31 Tivy suggests that grouse moors in Scotland cover about 1.214 million hectares and that average yield is about one brace to 4/5 hectares in the Eastern Highlands, dropping to 10/20 hectares in the west. On this data, the figures given above are probably conservative but it must be emphasised that overall quantitative data of recent origin is lacking. cf Tivy in Tivy (ed) 1973 p 91.

32 D MacLean. Description of shooting and fishings . . . the property of the Duke of Sutherland, Golspie 1905. Cited in O'Dell and Walton, The Highlands and Islands of Scotland, Nelson 1962, Appendix A.

33 Strath of Kildonan — proposals for development. HIDB (1970).

34 Not that grouse and sheep are entirely complementary. The early gathering of lambs from some hills in the area (eg in Sutherland) — and early sales associated with this practice — may owe something to the start of the grouse shooting season on August 12th.

gun day are reasonably common but there is considerable variation depending on the type of shooting offered, the expected bag, and location. The value of the birds as game probably averages £1 per brace, and the total output can therefore be estimated at £4 per brace, giving a value of output of approximately £400,000 for Scotland and £80,000 for the Highlands.

Other game

By comparison with red deer and grouse, other game species are relatively unimportant, though capable of improvement in selected parts of the region. Roe deer and Sika deer are of growing significance. Duck and geese are significant locally, as are hares, pheasants, partridge, blackgame, capercaillie, woodcock and snipe.

Environmental constraints on existing and potential land use

Climate

Climatic factors represent the major environmental constraint on biological production in the Highlands. The map prepared by Bibby[35] suggests that under a half million acres of land in the region has moderate, slight, or no climatic limitations. The remaining 8½ million acres thus have severe or very severe climatic limitations. Only the favoured coastal parts of the Moray and Cromarty Firths have no, or only slight, climatic limitations. Climate is of course an omnibus term; in the context of the Highlands and Islands, rainfall, temperature and windspeed are the important factors to consider.

According to hydrological data covering a 30 year period,[36] the higher parts of Wester Ross, West Inverness-shire and North Argyll have a mean annual rainfall in excess of 79 inches. These high averages are associated with the higher land exposed to the south-west, which presents a barrier to the incoming frontal systems from the Atlantic. In the leeward rain shadow of these higher areas, and at lower altitudes, averages of 63-79 inches are common. The Long Isle, North Skye, Inverness and Argyll Islands and South Argyll have 47-63 inches, while Caithness, Sutherland and the rest of the area have 31-47 inches, exceptions being small areas around the Moray Firth, the North of Lewis and around Wick, which have less than 31 inches. Moreover, because of low temperatures, potential evaporation in Scotland is very low and 'with only 400 mm (16in) average annual evapo-transpiration has, with north-west Scandinavia, the lowest values in Europe except for the extreme north of Norway'[37] Over most of the Highlands and Islands there

35 Bibby in Tivy (ed) (1973) p 56.

36 Hydrological Memo No 37, Meteorological Office. Cited in Tivy (1973) p 17.

37 Miller, in Tivy (ed) (1973) p 19.

is said to be no 'potential water deficit',[38] and soils are at or near field capacity for a high proportion of the year.[39] The driest parts of the region correspond closely to those with the most favourable geology — Orkney, Caithness and the Moray Firth. Snowfall is also important in the region, particularly towards the north-east and on the higher ground. The average annual number of days with snow observed to fall in the region on ground below 200 feet ranges from 15 in South Argyll and Mull to 35 in Caithness.[40] Theoretical advantages of insulation and slow release of moisture may exist but are dependent on more stable winter conditions than have been common in recent years when heavy snowfall has often been followed by rapid thaw and then freezing conditions.[41] On the higher ground, where exposed to prevailing winds, snow cover may be rapidly removed, thereby exposing the vegetation to frost damage.

The moderating effect of maritime climate on temperature in the British Isles is well known and the mean seasonal differences in temperature at sea level are little different in the Highlands and Islands from the rest of Scotland, although summer temperatures in the north and west of the region tend to be somewhat lower. As with rainfall, however, relief is an important factor, and the lapse rate in the region is considered to be rather greater than the standard 3.3°F per 1,000 feet.

Above about 1,000 feet in the west, and 2,000 feet in the centre and east, temperatures are more often below freezing than above.[42] Temperature and latitude (through the effect on radiation) combine to limit the length of the growing season in the Highlands and Islands. *Hunt* suggests a reduction in the growing season by seven days per degree latitude northward at sea level. He cites work by Gloyne which further suggests that at 1,000 feet the growing season will be 36 days less and at 2,000 feet 72 days less than at sea level.[43] Probably less than 30 per cent of the region has a growing season in excess of six months and in parts of Sutherland, Ross and Cromarty and Inverness, altitude reduces the growing season to less than five months in the year. Latitude itself implies that the growing season in Shetland will be roughly one month less than at Stirling.

Wind, being associated with the maritime weather influence, is most

38 The 'potential water deficit' is defined as the sum of the monthly differences between precipitation (P) and potential evapo-transpiration (E), for those months in the year when E > P. cf Ragg in Tivy (ed) p 41.

39 Nevertheless, the experiĕnce of the HIDB has been that soil moisture can be limiting in certain cases and at certain times on the west coast, in the western islands, and in the Moray Firth. See also Chapter 4 and Plant, J A (1970).

40 From Manley (1952) cited in Miller *loc cit*. For ground above 200 feet one day for each 50 feet above 200 feet should be added.

41 This thesis receives some support from a recent paper by Green, 'The transient snow-line in the Scottish Highlands' in 'Weather', July 1975.

42 Miller *op cit* p 21. Based on evidence of periglacial studies.

43 Hunt in Tivy (ed) (1973) p 131.

strongly felt on the west coasts and the islands and at altitude. The average windspeed is greater than 18 mph (in excess of moderate strength on the Beaufort scale) for 40 per cent of the year at Lerwick, and at Kirkwall and Wick for 29 per cent of the year, as compared with 19 per cent of the year at Kinloss in Morayshire.[44] At the Butt of Lewis, winds reach the threshold of gale force (24 mph) 29 per cent of the time.[45] Windspeed, and the salt-spray carried by the winds, damages vegetation in exposed conditions and limits the potential for forestry in the Western and Northern Isles and generally along the West and North Coast. Thus, according to *Miller*, the commercial planting limit in the West is on average about 215 feet in contrast with about 1,000 feet in the East.[46] In these circumstances, shelter — either natural of man-made — assumes considerable (if largely unquantified) significance.

The discussion of climatic limitations has inevitably involved reference to altitude and relief, which are highly significant in determining rainfall, snow cover, temperature, windspeed and, to some extent, light intensity. Height, slope, and aspect are all important and *Ormiston* notes dramatic differences between summer and spring temperatures on north and south facing slopes of different gradient. A range of 25 per cent is given for 20° slopes in March according to whether they are south or north facing.[47] About 60 per cent (or 5½ million acres) of the surface area of the region lies over 1000 feet and 10 per cent lies over 2000 feet. By far the major part of this area of high ground will be above the effective tree line and utilisation possibilities restricted to grazing for sheep and deer when climate permits and, of course, to high level recreational pursuits.

Geology and Soils

The geological maps of Scotland suggest the dominance of Metamorphic rocks — Schists, Gneiss, and Orthogneiss — of the Moine and Lewisian Series.[48] Perhaps 65 to 75 per cent of the Northern Highlands have these rocks beneath the soil or outcropping through it.[49] Granite is also common. These rocks resist weathering and produce acid soils, usually of a very stony, sandy loam texture, although the surface horizon is very often

44 Swan and Senior (1972) pp 12, 42 and 71.

45 Miller *loc cit*.

46 Miller *loc cit*.

47 Ormiston (1973) p 34. It is not stated whether the data refers to soil temperatures or to air temperatures.

48 Geological Map in Institute of Geological Sciences (1960) and Bickmore and Shaw, The Atlas of Great Britain and Northern Ireland OUP (1963).

49 Institute of Geological Sciences (1960). The Northern Highlands exclude the area to the south and east of the Great Glen and are not therefore coterminous with the Highlands and Islands. Nevertheless, this area has very similar characteristics to those described.

Table 2-14. Highlands & Islands: Principal Environmental Parameters

Area	Area in '000 acres	*Relief*		*Geology & Soil*			*Growing Season*		
		Land over 2000 ft	1000 ft to 2000 ft	% Sedimentary Rocks	% Glacial Drift	% Peat	<5 months	5-6 months	>6 months
SHETLAND	352.3	Nil	<1%	12%	10%	53%	Nil	100%	Nil
ORKNEY	240.8	Nil	2%	100%	50%	17%	Nil	80%	20%
CAITHNESS	438.8	<1%	<5%	>95%	40%	61%	neg	75%	25%
SUTHERLAND	1,297.9	5%	20%	10%	20%	32%	<10%	>80%	10%
ROSS-SHIRE	1,977.3	15%	60%	20%	20%	16%	10%	70%	20%
INVERNESS-SHIRE	2,695.1	20%	75%	3%	15%	5%	15%	70%	15%
ARGYLL	1,990.5	10%	30%	5%	10%	2%	neg	30%	70%
CROFTING COUNTIES	8,992.8	10%	50%	18%	20%	16%	10%	70%	20%

Sources: *Relief* Estimated from relief maps.
Geology Sedimentary Rocks. Estimated from Geological Maps in Bickmore and Shaw (1963).
Glacial Drift. Estimated from drift maps.
Peat. Derived from Jowsey in Tivy (ed) (1973) p 111.
Growing Season Estimated from an inspection of the map in Tivy (ed) 1973 p 16 (after Gregory 1954 from Watson and Sissons, 1964).

Note:
The estimates in the above table were prepared for us by Ardern and Fallows of the Planning and Research Division of the Highlands and Islands Development Board. They must be regarded as rough approximations only.

peat of varying depth. Basic and intermediate igneous rocks of Skye, Rhum, Eigg, Mull, the Ardnamurchan peninsula and the Lorne plateau of Argyll are exceptions, and these tend to produce stony loams.[50] The best soils in the region from an agricultural point of view are derived from Old Red Sandstone, occurring mainly along the eastern seaboard and running through Orkney, Caithness and the Moray Firth Area, but also in small areas along the north coast (Tongue, Strathnaver), in Urquhart and at the foot of Glen Garry in the Great Glen, in Cowal, and in Southend, Kintyre. Probably less than 12 per cent of the land area of the region overlays Old Red Sandstone. Limestone formations also produce pockets of good soil in the region and outcrops occur in Argyll (for example, Lismore, Kintyre, Islay and Lochaber) and along the line of the Moine Thrust from Durness to Skye, and in the Tingwall Valley in Shetland. Soil type is not always related to parent rock; principal modifications are due to raised beaches, glacial drift and, particularly in the Western Isles, sand-blow, together with the effects of man's intrusion. While these modifications are locally important, regionally the most significant feature remains the dominance of the hard metamorphic rocks which give it its mountainous aspect and which make cultivation and management difficult.

The Classification of Land Capability

Mapping of Soils and Land Capability covers only a small proportion of the Highlands and Islands, work having been done by the Macaulay Institute for Soil Research in Caithness and Orkney, the Moray Firth area and, in association with the Highland Board's Land Use Surveys programme, in Mull and Ardnamurchan. The system of land use capability classification used by the Institute in Scotland is described by Bibby and Mackney and involves seven main classes, each (with the exception of Class 1) having up to 25 sub-classes according to the type of limitation experienced.[51] The system follows that developed by the USDA in that it is based on relationships (known or inferred) between growth and management of crops and the environmental factors affecting growth and management. The greater the limitations imposed by climate, relief, slope, aspect, and soil, the lower the capability and the higher (numerically) the capability class. Thus Class 1 land has very minor limitations and is suitable for all the usual crops grown in the UK, including horticultural crops, while Class 6 and 7 land has very severe or extremely severe limitations with no cropping and with improvement for agriculture or forestry possible only on selected sites of Class 6 land. Generally speaking, land suited to cultivation and other uses is included in Classes 1-4, whilst land not suited to cultivation is included in Classes 5-7.

50 Bibby in Tivy (1973) p 58.

51 Bibby and Mackney (1969).

Consideration of geology, relief and climate leads Bibby to conclude that 'throughout most of the Highland area the highest land use capability Class is 4 . . . whilst the majority of the land falls into Classes 5 . . . , 6, and 7 . . .'.[52] In Caithness and Orkney, although soils are comparatively favourable, the highest land use capability Class is 3, with principal limitations being set by exposure to wind and wetness of the soils.[53] The Moray Firth area, however, contains the most northerly Class 1 land so far mapped in Britain, albeit in limited quantities. According to Ormiston, the Moray Firth Development Area has 44,630 acres of Class 1 and 2 land out of a total of 614,133 acres in agricultural use in 1971, of which some 220,000 acres are below 200 feet.[54] The area of high quality land is consequently limited, accounting as it does for only about 20 per cent of the land below 200 feet and just over 7 per cent of the entire Moray Firth Area as defined. This feature of the area has considerable significance for zoning for industrial and other urban uses.[55]

The island of Mull exemplifies a very different and more typically 'Highland' situation than the Moray Firth area. Limitations imposed by climatic factors are such that no soils display the flexibility of use demanded by Classes 1-3, and the highest Class is 4.[56] The total agricultural area of Mull is 196,000 acres but the vast majority of this area would be Class 6 or 7 land and probably only some 10 per cent of land on Mull as a whole would belong to Classes 4 or 5. The Board's Mull Report estimated that some 4,600 acres of lower ground could be brought into cultivation or be improved by cultivation techniques, and at least 8,000 acres of better hill land would respond to surface regeneration treatment. By and large, climatic factors limit the use of land on Mull to grass production, forestry and deer. The quality of land in Ardnamurchan and Morvern is less favourable for agriculture than on Mull and proportions of improvable land are correspondingly lower.[57]

The Potential for Land Improvement

Past estimates of improvable land over the Highlands and Islands as a whole vary considerably, which is not surprising in the absence of overall classifi-

52 Bibby in Tivy (ed) (1973) p 60.

53 Bibby *loc cit*.

54 Ormiston (1973) pp 84, 58, 20 respectively.

55 Ormiston (1973). This study was sponsored by the HIDB.

56 Island of Mull — Survey and proposals for Development. HIDB Special Report No 10 (1973).

57 The HIDB is one of the few bodies within the UK which uses this Classification System as an aid in determining land use policies. We would agree with the Board in preferring an approach which aims at identifying *potential* use, rather than one which is based on *existing* use (such as that employed by DAFS). Nevertheless, we have some reservations about the procedures involved and these are set out in Appendix 2A.

cation of the land and, frequently, the differing definitions which are employed. Moreover, global estimates of this kind are vulnerable to changes in relative prices and costs and the discovery of new techniques. Estimates based on the Zuckerman Report (1957)[58] suggested that some 100,000 acres might be immediately suitable and sufficiently accessible for reclamation.[59] However, the Highland Advisory Panel (1964) felt that this 'greatly under-estimated the possibilities in view of the considerable developments in techniques in recent years . . .' .[60]

On the assumption that the relative returns to livestock rearing will be maintained closer to those of the early 1970s rather than, say, 1974/75, it seems likely that the Zuckerman figure of 100,000 acres is a minimum estimate. As Chapter 1 reveals, there are 58,000 acres classified as 'crops and grass' on insignificant holdings alone.[61] The problem here is not so much one of land potential, but the conditions on which land is occupied. A similar general point could be made about some of the very large holdings which, although not 'insignificant' in the technical sense, are primarily managed for non-agricultural purposes.

On the basis of the work done in Mull and other areas of North Argyll, it seems possible that up to 100,000 acres — or 7 per cent of the area of rough and hill grazings — could be improved in Argyll alone. For the remaining Highland counties, the proportion of improvable ground is likely to be lower than this but, even at 3 per cent of the area of rough and hill grazings, would amount to over 150,000 acres. On this basis, a long term target of 250,000 acres of land improvement in the Highlands would not seem unrealistic.

At the farm level, the Hill Farming Research Organisation has pioneered new techniques of hill pasture improvement and management, and this work has demonstrated the feasibility of improvement on hill farms. At Lephinmore in Argyll, a programme of hill pasture improvement and fencing to control grazing has succeeded in raising the number of breeding ewes from 205 to 433 on 1,000 acres, and the lambing percentage from 60 to 98. The total weight of lambs weaned has increased from some 3 kg per acre to nearly 11 kg per acre. Net investment in stock and improvements has been of the order of £7,000, whilst Gross Margins have increased by

58 Natural Resources (Technical) Committee (1957). The estimate was cited in the Report on Land Use in the Highlands and Islands prepared by the Advisory Panel on the Highlands and Islands, p 28 (HMSO 1964).

59 Reclamation is used here in its wider sense 'describing operations which may range from the simple application of lime and fertilisers with surface reseeding, to operations involving deep drainage, ploughing, rotovating and subsequent treatment with fertilisers, leading to extensive and varied cropping'. Report, *op cit* pp 27/28.

60 Report, *loc cit*.

61 The total area of agricultural land (excluding common grazings) occupied by insignificant holdings is 641,221 acres and, of this, 455,579 acres were on the 36 insignificant holdings greater than 5,000 acres in extent. See also Table 2-19 below.

about £1,000, all at 1974 prices.[62] In North Argyll, a co-operative improvement scheme based partly on the HFRO 'model' was the subject of an application to the European Economic Community for grant aid under the FEOGA individual projects scheme. The viability of this scheme had to be carefully established. This project included some 21,231 acres of land regeneration and 7,421 acres of bracken control over a five year period and the area of land to be improved represented about 7½ per cent of the total area of rough grazings on the 64 farms involved.[63]

Given the estimates of improvable land above and the possible increases in lamb output which, on the basis of the experience of the HFRO, could be associated with such improvement, an increase in the regional output of sheep meat of between 20 and 25 per cent would seem to be a realistic target in the medium term, and the figure could be higher than this in the longer term.

Potential afforestation

The Report of the Advisory Panel on the Highlands and Islands suggested that there was 'well over 1,000,000 acres of plantable land in the Highlands, of which on current standards about 500,000 would be 'cleared' from agriculture . . .'.[64] However, the panel were also aware of the difficulties . . . 'In certain parts of the Highlands, such as North-West Sutherland, the amount of land of reasonable quality is so limited that if it is taken for forestry this could only be at the cost of near extinction of the agriculture'.[65] Nevertheless they felt that areas — such as Strath Oykell — existed where the possibility of 'parallel' development was such as to allow the development of both agriculture and forestry, and concluded that an afforestation programme by the Forestry Commission of at least 20,000 acres per annum in addition to private planting of about 3,000 acres per annum would be fully justified without 'excessive' inroads into agriculture.

Potential in horticulture

Potential also exists in new fields, including horticulture, some of which have been tried in recent years.[66] Despite the environmental limitations of the

62 Lephinmore Research Station Handbook, HFRO (1975). See also Cunningham J M M, The Biological Resources of the Highlands. Paper to the British Association for the Advancement of Science Meeting, Stirling. September 1974. Published in the Annual Report of the Highland Fund, 1974/75.

63 The application of the North Argyll Agricultural Development Society Ltd (as it is called) was prepared jointly by the Highlands and Islands Development Board and the West of Scotland College of Agriculture in co-operation with the members of the Society. The figures given above are based on the original application to the EEC.

64 Report (1964) p 37

65 Report *loc cit*.

66 See also Chapter 4.

area described above, there are relatively small, but locally significant, areas of land which may possess bioclimatic advantages of sufficient magnitude to offset the economic disadvantages of locating production so far from the principal markets. Two main factors are involved in this theory. First the influence of the Gulf Stream on sea temperatures and the effect of this on coastal mesoclimates, which means the absence of frost and, in low lying locations close to the shore, the possibility of longer growing seasons. Since solar radiation in the Highlands and Islands is comparable with that at lower latitudes — especially during the main growing period — temperature effects are important in determining the success of biological production.[67] Nor was water stress thought likely to be a significant factor in such areas.[68] Indeed, *Waister* suggested that, although in general crops in England showed higher yields than in Scotland, for tulips higher bulking rates were achieved in the North in experiments where the major variables were temperature and radiation.[69] The seasonal factor involved the favourable effect of climate on the incidence of pests and diseases — particularly the low incidence of aphids which spread virus diseases.[70] This effect largely explains the pre-eminence of Scotland as a producer of high quality seed potatoes.

Loss of Agricultural Land

The overall possibilities for development of primary land use have not been significantly impaired by losses of land to urban or industrial use, which, as Table 2-15 shows, were responsible for only 1 per cent of all net losses of

Table 2-15. Net Losses of Agricultural Land in the Highlands and Islands 1965-1974

	Total 1965-74 Acres	*Average Annual Loss*
Loss to:		
Roads, Housing and Industrial Development	3,056	340
Recreation	1,393	155
Mineral Workings	549	61
Hydro-Electric and Water Boards	255	28
Service Departments	117(a)	13(a)
Forestry	210,523	23,391
Other	3,366(a)	374(a)
Total Net Loss	*212,293*	*23,588*

Note:
(a) Gain

Source: DAFS

67 Gloyne R W, Crop Production in Higher Latitudes, Maritime Areas, Int J Biometeor, 1973, Vol 17 No 4 pp 349-354.

68 Waister P D, Climatic Limitations on Horticultural Production, with Particular Reference to Scottish Conditions. Int J Biometeor, 1973, Vol 17 No 4 pp 379-383.

69 Waister, *loc cit*.

70 Waister, *loc cit*.

agricultural land in the region during the period 1965-66 to 1973-74. The rest is accounted for by losses to forestry.

Losses to roads, housing and industrial development have been locally important, particularly in the Moray Firth Area. The fact that losses in this category tend to be from the best quality farm land has given rise to public concern, particularly in the Moray Firth area. The HIDB commissioned a study in 1969 in order to assess the impact of present and likely industrial and urban growth on the agricultural area and make recommendations which would help those concerned to ensure that the agricultural industry would develop in harmony with other industry. According to the report on this study,[71] the Moray Firth Development Area, which extends from Tain in the north to Ardersier in the south, contains about 45,000 acres of Class 1 and 2 land on the Macaulay classification. Under the Jack Holmes proposals,[72] a total of 11,000 acres, of which 3,500 acres was Class 1 and 2 land, would be required for housing, industry and related non-agricultural development assuming a build-up of population from about 60,000 to 254,000 — the estimated 'capacity' of the area in question. In fact, the areas of land zoned between 1967 and 1974 amount to some 7,200 acres, of which about 2,800 acres is Class 1 and 2 land, whilst the areas of land actually developed or with valid planning permission over this period amounted to about 2,800 acres, of which about 900 acres was Class 1 and 2 land. Although the forward zoning allocates greater acreages of land to industry than to housing and public utilities, in practice housing has been responsible for the greatest loss of land to date in the area, followed by industry.[73] Framing a consistent long term land use plan involving the switch from agricultural to industrial or urban use is a complex matter which requires that a long term view is taken on the value of good quality agricultural land from the regional and national standpoint. Given the prospect of more rapid industrial growth than was envisaged at the time when Ormiston was writing, it is all the more important that such decisions are taken with great care, and within the context of an overall, agreed, strategy for the region.[74]

Land Prices and Rents

Land prices fail to reflect the true returns from land use because of market distortions which result from such factors as fiscal conditions, the social

71 Ormiston J H, The Moray Firth: An agricultural Study. HIDB Special Report No 9, April 1973.

72 Jack Holmes Planning Group. 'The Moray Firth — a plan for growth in a sub-region of the Scottish Highlands'. Prepared for the HIDB in 1967/68.

73 However, the bulk of zoned but 'underdeveloped' land in Classes 1 and 2 is for industrial use, and roughly half of this is located in the Invergordon area alone. Much of the new housing proposed is on Class 3 land.

74 See also page 84 below.

status of landownership, private amenity valuation, the likelihood of planning permission, and the low volume of land on the market. These 'distortions' are of greater importance in the Highlands and Islands than elsewhere and this has been reflected in relatively high land prices, at least until 1974.[75] Recent proposals relating to the taxation of wealth and capital transfers have illustrated how quickly a change in fiscal conditions can affect the market valuation of land in the region — particularly in the case of sporting estates. Rents on the other hand are subject to certain controls which tend to ensure that they reflect no more than the agricultural value of land over a period of time. On hill sheep farms, rents tend to be fixed at a rate per ewe rather than per acre, and although separate data are not available for the Highlands and Islands rents per acre and per ewe tend to be significantly lower than the Scottish average. Table 2-16 shows the change in prices for agricultural land in the Highlands as compared with Scotland in recent years.

These figures illustrate both the dramatic rise in land prices over this period — particularly for hill and upland farms — and the lower average prices for farms in the Highlands and Islands. They also show the very low

Table 2-16. Sales of Equipped Farms over 20 acres — Highlands and Islands and Scotland, 1963, 1964, 1970 and 1972

	Sales with Vacant Possession only			
	1963	*1964*	*1970*	*1972*
Crofting Counties				
Hill & Upland Farms				
No of Transactions	25	16	31	26
Aggregate Acreage, Acres	14,986	20,390	6,547	4,935
Price/Acre £	*12.5*	*7.7*	*21.6*	*54.6*
Other Types of Farms				
No of Transactions	34	34	34	28
Aggregate Acreage, Acres	5,861	4,530	3,584	3,757
Price/Acre £	*36.6*	*41.8*	*59.6*	*72.0*
Scotland				
Hill & Upland Farms				
No of Transactions	72	70	96	64
Aggregate Acreage, Acres	44,041	46,765	32,197	20,785
Price/Acre £	*21*	*24*	*49*	*71*
Other Types of Farms				
No of Transactions	384	401	294	267
Aggregate Acreage, Acres	54,712	67,363	41,156	43,446
Price/Acre £	*93*	*100*	*135*	*180*

Source: For Scottish Data, MacKenzie A M in SAE Vol XXIV — 1974.
Crofting Counties data has been compiled from DAFS records by J R A Cumming.

75 See also Chapter 3. Using market valuations for land, the gross return on landlord's capital has probably been less than 2 per cent over most of the Highlands and Islands. See also McEwan L V, SAE Vol XXI — 1971, Table 6.

turnover in agricultural land in the region. At the time of writing (1975) there has been a considerable reduction in the price of land in the region — particularly for sporting estates, but also for hill and upland farms. This has been partly due to the general economic situation and the depression in hill and upland farming and partly — and probably more significantly — to the proposed capital transfer and wealth taxes which will remove or reduce some of the previous fiscal advantages of landownership. High — and rapidly rising — land prices probably encouraged investment of a largely speculative nature and prevented at least some young farmers from entering the industry. To the extent that this has been true, a return to lower and more stable land prices would have advantages for regional development.

Land ownership, tenure and control

Whatever the economic potential of land in the region, its use will be ultimately determined by the objectives, financial circumstances and rights of those who own or control the land resources. Land ownership in the Highlands is highly uneven and large areas of land are held by relatively few families. This is only imperfectly indicated by the official statistics, due to the fact that these are collated on the basis of farm 'units' rather than on the basis of ownership. Nor do the official data reflect the true locus of control over land since several units may be owned and/or managed by a single individual, whilst one unit may contain both owner-occupied and leased land. The figures nevertheless show that about 82 per cent of the land area is contained in just under 6 per cent of the holdings in the Highlands and Islands, whilst in Scotland as a whole a similar proportion of the land area is contained in about 25 per cent of holdings. The highly skewed distribution for the Highlands and Islands is of course partly a reflection of the type of land use carried out over the major part of the area, which comprises hill and mountain, and also of the special place of crofting in the region. Nearly 60 per cent of 'units' in the Highlands and Islands are below 50 acres, as compared with 36 per cent in Scotland. In terms of the crops and grass acreage, only about 10 per cent of units in the Highlands and Islands would have more than 100 acres of crops and grass, as compared with nearly 38 per cent for Scotland.

Complete records of land ownership and tenure are hard to compile in Scotland due to the outdated and cumbersome system of registration of title.[76] Moreover, in considering the effect of a title to land on land use, it

76 Even if the detailed records held in the Register of Sasines were consulted, this would only be the start of a long investigation in view of the extent of 'hidden' ownership in the region whereby Trusts and Companies of various kinds obscure the locus of true control over property. Moreover, titles in land are not necessarily recorded in the Register; nor do these titles necessarily embody a complete description giving the areas of land held.

Table 2-17. Distribution of Agricultural Units and Acreage by Total Acreage Size Groups, June 1972 Crofting Counties and Scotland

	Crofting Counties				*Scotland*			
	No of Units		Acreage		No of Units		Acreage	
Size Group	No	%	'000 Acres	%	No	%	'000 Acres	%
<5 acres	1,081	8.53	3.68	0.06	2,129	5.61	6.50	0.05
5-9¾ acres	1,767	13.94	12.30	0.19	3,273	8.63	22.88	0.16
10-49¾ acres	4,707	37.14	114.74	1.82	8,501	22.41	214.81	1.52
50-249¾ acres	3,208	25.32	352.29	5.58	14,862	39.18	1,904.72	13.45
250-1,249¾ acres	1,158	9.14	634.48	10.04	7,388	19.48	3,617.86	22.55
1,250-4,999¾ acres	492	3.88	1,281.74	20.29	1,397	3.68	3,352.37	23.68
> 5,000 acres	259	2.04	3,918.33	62.02	380	1.00	5,139.01	36.30
TOTAL	12,672	100.00	6,317.56	100.00	37,930	100.00	14,258.15	100.00

Source: Agricultural Statistics, 1972. Tables 18, 19, 22, 23. The data refer to 'significant' units only.

Table 2-18. Distribution of Agricultural Units and Acreage by Crops and Grass Acreage Size Groups, June 1972 Crofting Counties and Scotland

	Crofting Counties				*Scotland*			
	No of Units		Acreage		No of Units		Acreage	
Size Group	No	%	'000 Acres	%	No	%	'000 Acres	%
0	551	4.35		—	1,004	2.65	—	—
¼-4¾ acres	2,335	18.43	7.18	1.32	3,546	9.35	10.35	0.25
5-14¾ acres	3,626	28.61	31.61	5.80	6,073	16.01	53.19	1.28
15-49¾ acres	3,263	25.75	92.13	16.91	6,621	17.46	197.53	4.74
50-99¾ acres	1,505	11.88	105.78	19.42	6,470	17.06	473.80	11.38
100-299¾ acres	1,131	8.93	182.27	33.46	10,945	28.86	1,878.87	45.13
300-499¾ acres	181	1.43	68.07	12.49	2,326	6.13	877.32	21.07
500-999¾ acres	73	0.58	47.01	8.63	858	2.26	555.30	13.34
>1,000 acres	7	0.06	10.74	1.97	87	0.23	117.04	2.81
TOTAL	12,672	100.00	544.80	100.00	37,930	100.00	4,163.40	100.00

Source: Agricultural Statistics, 1972 Scotland. The data refers to 'significant' units only.

Table 2-19. Land Tenure in the Highlands and Islands, 1970

Holdings (No) and Acreage in '000 Acres

	Significant Units[a]		*Insignificant Units*[a]		*All Units*	
	Holdings	*Area*	*Holdings*	*Area*	*Holdings*	*Area*
Tenanted						
Crofts	7,450	489.9	7,197	69.2	14,647	559.1
Leasehold & other tenanted	1,803	2,058.6	1,207	68.6	3,010	2,127.1
Common Grazings[c]	(848)c	1,212.1	b	b	b	1,212.1
Total Tenanted[d]	9,253	3,760.6	8,404	137.8	17,657	3,898.4
Owner-Occupied						
Crofts[b]	534	156.9	359	46.7	893	203.6
Other Units	2,920	3,632.7	1,467	456.6	4,387	4,089.3
Total Owner-Occupied	3,454	3,789.6	1,826	503.3	5,280	4,292.9
Total — All Units[e]	*12,707*	*7,550.2*	*10,230*	*641.1*	*22,937*	*8,191.3*

Notes:

a As defined by DAFS in 1970. Holdings below 27 standard man days are regarded as 'insignificant'.

b It is not possible to distinguish between rights in common grazings held by tenant crofters, owner-occupier crofters and significant and insignificant croft units.

c Holdings here refers to the number of common grazings and this figure is not included in the totals.

d Includes area of common grazings.

e There are some 1900 holdings of 'like economic status' to crofts in the region.

Source: Based on data supplied by DAFS

Table 2-20. Land Tenure in the Highlands and Islands showing average holding size and Distribution of Holdings and Area by type of Tenure, 1970

	Average Size of Holding (Acres)		Distribution of Holdings & Acreage			
			% of Holdings		*% of Area*	
	All Units	*Significant Only*	*All Units*	*Significant Only*	*All Units*	*Significant Only*
Tenanted Area						
Crofts	38	66	63.9	58.6	6.8	6.5
Leasehold	707	1,142	13.1	14.2	26.0	27.3
Common Grazings	(1,429)	(1,429)	—	—	14.8	16.1
All tenanted units	221[a]	406[a]	77.0	72.8	47.6[a]	49.8[a]
Owner Occupied Area						
Crofts	228	294	3.9	4.2	2.5	2.1
Other O/O	932	1,244	19.1	23.0	49.9	48.1
All owner occupied	813	1,097	23.0	27.2	52.4	50.2
All Units	*357*	*594*	*100.0*	*100.0*	*100.0*	*100.0*
All Crofts (incl. common)	*127*	*233*	*67.8*	*62.8*	*24.1*	*24.7*

Notes:
For general notes, see Table 2-19.

a Includes common grazings area

Source: Derived from Table 2-19.

is necessary to go beyond ownership and examine tenure since most forms of tenure now give considerable security to the occupier, thereby removing much control over land use on such units from the owner to the occupier. Thus, for example, the question of who controls land use on a large estate which is largely let under crofting tenure is entirely different from that relating to a large estate which is entirely owner-occupied.

Tables 2-19 and 2-20 show the tenure situation in the Highlands and Islands and demonstrate the significance of crofting as a factor influencing the average size of holding in the region.

Land which is owner-occupied thus accounts for about half of the total agricultural area of the Highlands and Islands, with the remaining area divided almost equally between units on crofting tenure and units on leasehold tenure. Taking the region as a whole, there is little difference between the average size of non-croft leasehold units and owner-occupied units, although considerable differences do arise at the county level. Owner-occupied units tend to be about twice the size of tenanted units in Argyll, Inverness and Ross and Cromarty, slightly larger in Sutherland, and slightly smaller in Orkney, Caithness and Shetland.

Public land ownership in one form or another extends to approximately 1.6 million acres, or about 18 per cent of the total land of the region. Most of this land is owned by the Forestry Commission, who held some 1.2 million acres in 1972.

Table 2-21. Estimated Public and Private Land Ownership in the Highlands and Islands circa 1970

(Million acres)

	Agricultural Area[a]		*Forestry*		
	Leased	*In Hand*	*Planted*	*Other*[b]	*Total*
Publicly owned[c]	0.49[e]	0.61[f]	0.35	0.15	1.60
Privately owned[d]	3.41	3.68	0.14	0.16	7.39
Total	3.90	4.29	0.49	0.31	8.99

Notes:

a Including deer forest and common grazings.

b Includes Cairngorm estate and other non-agricultural land such as towns, roads, airfields, defence establishments, publicly owned factory sites, etc.

c Includes land owned by the Secretary of State (Department of Agriculture and Forestry Commission), the HIDB, Local Authorities, the Nature Conservancy, Defence Departments, the British Airports Authority (previously the CAA).

d Calculated as a residual item by deducting publicly owned land from the total land area in each category.

e Mainly on crofting tenure. Includes some 15,000 acres rented to the Colleges of Agriculture and the Hill Farming Research Organisation for purposes of research and demonstration.

f Includes deer forest and unplanted forestry land of about 550,000 acres in the hands of the Forestry Commission. Land owned by the Commission but leased for agriculture is generally managed by DAFS.

In terms of direct control over land use, these figures suggest that private landowners control 3.82 million acres of agricultural and forestry land, or about 44 per cent of the total area of land in these categories. In addition, they have some limited direct influence on land use over some 3.41 million acres leased by them to farmers and crofters. The public on the other hand has — through the various public bodies involved — direct control over just under 1 million acres or 11 per cent of agricultural and forestry land, and limited influence over just under ½ million acres leased mainly to crofters and other tenants. Practically all of this 1 million acres of land is in the direct control of the Forestry Commission, except to the extent that unplanted land is leased to sporting interests. Given that the prime objective of the Forestry Commission is to implement the nation's forestry planting programme, it is fair to conclude that the public have little direct say in agricultural land use except in the negative sense when DAFS prevents the Forestry Commission from purchasing land for forestry.

Bearing these factors in mind, we may now examine the structure of private landownership in the region so far as the limited data available permits.

Table 2-22. Private Landownership in the Highlands and Islands (Approx)

Size Category (Ownership Units)	*Total Acreage* ('000)	*Ownership Units*[a]	*No of Estates*
100,000 acres +	883	8	26
75-100,000	418	5	12
50-75,000	614	10	11
35-50,000	542	12	12
Total above	*2,457*	*35*	*61*

Note:
a Ownership units are estates or collections of estates owned by the same family or company.
Source: HIDB

We have derived these figures from analysis of the work by Millman on estate boundaries,[77] together with other information which was available within the Board.[78]

77 Millman R N (1969) The Marches of the Highland Estates SGM Vol 85, No 3.
Millman R N (1970) The Landed Properties of Northern Scotland SGM Vol 86, No 3.
Millman R N (1971) Outdoor Recreation in the Highland Countryside — A Study of Rural Management and Access for Public Recreation in Ten Selected Areas of the Highlands and Islands. Published in Cambridge by the author and subsequently distributed by the HIDB.

78 A similar exercise has recently been carried out by John McEwen who, however, included only five of the Crofting Counties and carried the analysis further down the size categories than we did. Although we would differ from McEwen on some of the detail given by him regarding individual holdings, his figures for estates over 30,000 acres correspond reasonably closely with the above — he gives 50 estates covering just over 2.7 million acres in this group. *McEwen* John, 'Highland Landlordism' in Brown (ed). The Red Paper on Scotland, EUSPB Edinburgh, 1975.

Some 35 families or companies with holdings over 36,000 acres therefore account for about one-third of all privately owned land in the Highlands and Islands, and consequently exert a considerable influence on land use in the region. What is not known is how much of this land is on crofting or leasehold tenure and therefore — at least from the agricultural point of view — the extent to which this influence is direct.[79]

Public control over changes in land use

Apart from the control over changes in land use on publicly owned land through the exercise of property rights, controls also exist over most primary changes of use proposed for privately owned land. Changes from primary to industrial or urban use are covered by the planning acts administered by the Regional or District Authorities, whilst changes from agriculture to forestry are now controlled by the Forestry Commission, except in the case of private forestry undertaken without grants. In both cases, DAFS tend to be consulted regarding the agricultural interest. Where the Forestry Commission proposes to acquire land for planting, clearance by DAFS is required prior to acquisition.

Three difficulties in the present system of controlling changes in land use were referred to in the Highland Board's evidence to the Select Committee on Scottish Affairs. First, the constraints presently applied tend to act as negative controls and not as a positive means of promoting regionally desirable developments. Secondly, decisions on changes in use tend to preclude a comprehensive approach and are usually made with reference to a choice between current use and the alternative under consideration.[80] Thirdly, despite work by special agencies like the Macaulay Institute and the Board, a coherent strategy of resource use in Scotland which would help to establish criteria for reference and guidance purposes are lacking.[81]

The problems of implementing a positive programme for land use in a country like Britain are formidable, but, as the case of Mull detailed in Chapter 4 emphasises, the costs of not undertaking positive steps to prepare and implement rural land use plans in areas which are highly dependent on primary activities based on the land can be substantial in both economic and human terms.

79 It appears that some 26 of these family holdings have crofts on them and in total they contain 5,890 registered crofts or almost one-third of the total number of registered crofts in the Crofting Counties.

80 Both DAFS and the Forestry Commission apply criteria which assess the choice between existing use and forestry and this largely excludes the possibility of other uses or a combination of uses on land so acquired. DAFS in its oral evidence to the Select Committee stated that they had 'a kind of standard formula, that below a certain (ewe) carry we are not going to think . . . of necessarily being opposed to forestry' (A2257). Land Resource Use in Scotland Vol III p 265.

81 Land Resource Use in Scotland, Vol III, pp 262-268.

Conclusions

Although forestry has been of growing importance to the region, it is agriculture which predominates over most of the Highlands in terms of primary land use and the output from the land. Within agriculture, the importance of extensive forms of livestock production in terms of both land use and output is related to the environmental limitations on biological production and these are reflected in the high proportion of rough grazings in the area. The possibilities of agricultural development over most of the region will therefore depend on the potential for the more efficient use of this type of ground by livestock. A high priority must be given to an increase in the quantity and quality of winter feed grown on the limited arable areas and to the improvement of areas of hill grazing to provide improved nutrition in the spring and autumn.

Taking the long view, there can be little doubt that improvement in the technical performance of cattle — and the output of meat associated with this — has been substantial, despite the fact that total cattle numbers have only recently returned to the levels recorded around 1800. But, whereas the largest advance in the cattle sector has probably taken place since the end of the last century, the reverse seems to be true of sheep, where physical productivity measured by lambing performance has shown little, if any, improvement, while the decline in wether production probably led to a decline in meat and wool output during this century.

The greater degree of concentration of arable farming within the Moray Firth area, and the increase in its technical performance, together with the relatively large increases in livestock output in the favoured grass-growing areas of Caithness and Orkney, must mean that the share of these areas in regional agricultural output has increased, while that of Sutherland, Argyll, and those parts of Inverness and Ross-shire beyond the Moray Firth area has been significantly reduced. It seems improbable that the switch in land use from agriculture to forestry and to deer which has taken place can be wholly to blame for these changes.

Notwithstanding the general environmental limitations of the region, studies of land capability and the potential for improvement have shown there to be significant areas of land which could be improved for agriculture, whilst research work by the Hill Farming Research Organisation and others has shown how these improvements can be economically used for the intensification of livestock production in hill areas. Statistics of the holdings classified as 'insignificant' from a production viewpoint also suggest an untapped potential which arises not from a lack of feasible uses, but more probably from the conditions under which the land is occupied. Although global estimates of improvable land and the production increases which might be associated with this are difficult to make, an increase in output of sheep meat of between 20 and 25 per cent would seem to be a realistic target in the medium term. Apart from agriculture, there is further potential in the area for forestry horticulture and game.

Losses of agricultural land to secondary and tertiary uses cannot be held responsible for a large part of any changes in the absolute or relative performance of Highland agriculture. However, the price which has until recently been paid for land coming on the market has certainly exceeded any realistic calculation of the discounted value of net income from the produce of that land, and this may have encouraged unproductive investment of a speculative nature and discouraged the entry of young farmers into the industry.

Of greater importance is the pattern of land ownership and control. Land is more unevenly distributed in the Highlands than in Scotland as a whole. Although this is partly a reflection of environmental factors, and the special place of crofting, the very large landholdings of a small number of family interests, whose objectives may place a low priority on productive development, may not only lead to underutilisation of the land, but also to a conflict with other interests in the community, which within the existing institutional framework is not likely to be resolved in a way which is consistent with regional development aims.

Public control over land use changes has been negative rather than positive in character. Although this may have helped to conceal conflict, it has acted against a comprehensive approach to land use. The criteria adopted have also proved to be less than adequate for the needs of the region. Although positive planning for land development would undoubtedly create problems in implementation, the cost of failing to take further steps in this direction could be particularly severe for areas such as the Western mainland and islands. In the Moray Firth area too, because of the high quality of land, particular care needs to be taken with future zoning for non-agricultural purposes.

APPENDIX 2A

Land Capability Assessment*

The policy-maker's requirements for Land Capability Assessment

In seeking to determine what improvements could be made to primary land use in particular areas, the policy-maker needs guidance as to (1) the biological possibilities of primary production and yields; (2) the probability of crop failures; (3) the feasibility and costs of 'improvement' — i.e. removing some or all of the constraints by investment in drainage, irrigation, shelter, application of chemicals, and by management practices — and the effects of such improvement on (1) and (2). Armed with this technical input he can assess the economic implications of pursuing alternative patterns of land use.

It can readily be appreciated that the requirements in areas containing virgin land, or hill land which is considered to be under or mis-used, are likely to be quite different from those in intensively used arable farming areas. For one thing, the **scale** requirements are quite different. For another, the biological possibilities tend to be much fewer and more easily defined.

The existing system of Land Capability Assessment

In Scotland there are at least three systems of land capability assessment in use. The DAFS has a system of land classification based largely on existing use and (so far as is possible) known production levels. The Forestry Commission has a system of defining land which is potentially 'plantable' given existing techniques and yield requirements; naturally this sytem deals only with forests. Neither of these assessments are publicly available in map form. The third system is that adopted by the Macaulay Institute for Soil Research and, since this system is designed to identify *potential* capability at moderately high levels of management, this system has been considered

*Our comments in this Appendix are not to be construed as a criticism of the work which has been carried out by the Macaulay Institute on behalf of the Board; it is normally up to the 'client' to specify the type of information required, although this can be difficult to arrange if the requirements differ materially from those agreed for a national programme of Land Capability Classification.

to come closest to providing the information needed by the HIDB in formulating long-term proposals for land use.

This system is described briefly in Chapter 2 and in detail by Bibby and Mackney in their 1969 paper. It is based on the Land Capability Classification developed by the Soil Conservation service of the United States Department of Agriculture (USDA), modified for use in the United Kingdom. In their paper, Bibby and Mackney point out that the system is interpretive and therefore 'subject to some degree of arbitrary decision'.

In essence, the USDA/Macaulay system amounts to a model which seeks to identify the range of biological possibilities at selected sites given the values of the variables relating to soil, site and climate (including rainfall, temperature, water balances). Thus 'It assesses land capability from known relationships between the growth and management of crops and physical factors of soil, site and climate'. (Bibby and Mackney, 1969, p 1). There is however an element of judgment involved in assessing such things as the 'average standard' management level in any area.

Problems from the user's point of view

From the point of view of a development agency working in the hill and upland situations of the Highlands and Islands, this system suffers, in our view, from the following deficiencies.

1 The process of survey is laborious and slow, partly as a result of the *scale* problems mentioned below.

2 The 'model' is unspecified — i.e. one cannot identify the value of parameters and variables and the precise interrelationship between them — and static. For instance, it is not possible to determine the difference in potential yields on one class of land compared with another; nor can one tell what effect a change in the parameters or variables will have in a quantitative sense.

3 It tends to be specifically agricultural, so that the relationship between capability classes may be valid for one form of production (grass) but not another (trees). (See also the Technical Monograph Assumptions 1 and 10).

4 In view of the absence of micro and meso-climatic data, the macro-climate is used as the basis for the classification system. In the USA, where climates tend to be stable over broad zones, this system may be quite adequate. In a maritime northern climate, where considerable variation in weather can occur within small areas, it seems to be too restrictive, although this may be inevitable in an area where the number of climate recording stations are few.

5 The system is not at present geared to the specific problem of land which is used mainly or entirely for grazing livestock. Animals also have climatic and other constraints which a *soil*-based system does not take account of. In practice, and where data on such things as exposure are

known or can be inferred, an attempt is however made by the surveyors to take this into account.

6 There are strong pressures for uniformity and comparability of classes between different parts of the UK which tend to reduce the value of the system in covering specific areas. For example, in the Highlands and Islands, where most of the land comes within Classes 5 and 6, the system is too narrow. Thus, where a hill farm consists entirely of Class 5 land, it is still important to know what piece of that land it might be best to improve. A relatively small area of naturally sheltered, well drained Class 5 land might be worth little in the Carse of Gowrie or the Vale of Evesham, but it may well be the key to success in Wester Ross. Against this, of course, the time and effort required to obtain this scale of data over wide areas might be a serious problem.

7 A related and final point concerns the published scale of the land capability maps. In hill and upland areas, the scale of 1" to 1 mile is an unsatisfactory compromise — being rather too small to identify particular *sites* for improvement, while at the same time requiring more detailed field work than a true reconnaissance survey.

It seems to us that a two-tier scale is required — one giving a reconnaissance survey of the whole area, the other following from this and at much larger scale dealing with arable and improvable areas of ground. It is at least arguable that the reconnaissance survey could be carried out more quickly, and at less cost, without reference to soil surveys but by interpretation of aerial photography (possibly remote sensing), physiographic and climatic data supplemented by such concrete information as is available on livestock performance (lambing percentages and weaning weights, stag weights, tree growth, etc). Such global reconnaissance surveys would identify areas suitable for more detailed surveys, which would also require a modified approach, particularly to allow for the importance of meso and micro-climate, the constraints on grazing livestock, and the need for a system of assessment which covers both grazing land and forestry land in more detail and which allows technical comparisons to be made between competing uses. To achieve this will require further work on climate at the meso and micro-scale. It will also need close liaison between bodies like the Macaulay Institute, the Hill Farming Research Organisation, the Colleges of Agriculture, the Meteorological Office, DAFS and the HIDB. It would also seem desirable — given that capability assessment can never be entirely objective and scientifically based — to carry out some monitoring of the system.

CHAPTER 3

Manpower and Productivity

The seven Crofting Counties contained about 19 per cent of Scotland's population in 1801 compared to 5½ per cent in 1971; the highest census population was recorded in 1851 at 395,540. By 1951, the total population had fallen to 286,000 and by 1961 to 278,000. Since then the population of the region has shown a modest increase of about 5,000, to 282,966.

Over half of the Highlands' population lives in the landward areas,[1] and, as Table 3-1 shows, these areas have been severely affected by depopulation in the post-war period. Even in the last decade, when overall population increased slightly, the landward population of the region fell by nearly 4,000, although this was a considerably lower rate of decline than in the previous decade.

Taking the mainland areas only, by far the largest increases in population were achieved in Inverness and Ross and Cromarty, and within these counties the increase largely occurred in the areas around the Moray and Cromarty Firths. Other mainland areas with significant population growth were the Fort William area (due largely to the pulp mill) and, to a lesser extent, the Oban area and the Mull of Kintyre. In the islands, the decline in population continued throughout the 1960s, although the rate of decline has moderated, even in the landward areas. Landward areas of the mainland, however, experienced a slight increase in population over the period 1961-1971 with marked intra-regional variations.

Despite an overall increase in population during the past decade, net emigration continued from the region as a whole[2] and was particularly marked in the landward areas and in the islands over this period. According to *Caird* . . . 'The larger of the burghs have benefited most . . . with Inverness, the Orkney and Zetland and some of the Cromarty Firth burghs attracting net in-migration exceeding their natural increase, and Inverness, Fort William, Fortrose, Invergordon and Tain all attracting an estimated net in-migration of over 15 per cent of their 1961 population between 1961 and 1971'.[3]

1 Landward population excludes conurbations and cities, large and small burghs. Small burghs are 'burghal areas of less than 10,000 inhabitants'. See also Census reports.

2 Caird (1972) Table 3.

3 Caird (1972) p 11.

Table 3-1. Population Change in the Crofting Counties 1951 to 1971

	1951	*% Change 1951-1961*	*1961*	*% Change 1961-1971*	*1971*
A. **Total Population**					
Mainland	191,591	+ 0.7	192,877	+ 5.5	203,549
Islands	94,195	− 9.7	85,071	− 6.7	79,417
Total	285,786	− 2.7	277,948	+ 1.8	282,966
B. **Landward Population**[a]					
Mainland	115,565	− 4.7	110,167	+ 1.6	111,909
Islands	76,472	− 12.9	66,587	− 8.6	60,889
Total	192,037	− 8.0	176,754	− 2.2	172,798

Note:
a See note 80 below for definition.

Source: Census Reports. Figures relate to *de facto* population.

The population growth experienced over the decade was thus confined in large part to the few growth centres where manufacturing industry had gained a foothold, while the landward areas of the region as a whole, still predominantly based on primary activities, continued to show a declining population. There is nothing new in this process, but in areas where the prospects of attracting manufacturing industry on any scale appear limited it represents a serious threat to the continued existence of a viable population.

Employment

Employment in the landward and predominantly rural areas in 1971 amounted to just under 64,000 in 1971 or some 58 per cent of total employment in the region.[4]

Total employment in the region increased marginally between 1961 and 1971, but employment based on primary land use — agriculture and horticulture, forestry and estate management — fell by some 5,500. This compares with a decline in total employment in the landward areas of 2,730. Employment declined not only in agriculture but also in forestry and — at least until 1966 — in land and estate management.

Information on agricultural employment is collected annually by the Department of Agriculture and Fisheries for Scotland at the June census. Until recently this information did not cover self-employed crofters and farmers who, given the structure of agricultural production in the region, constitute an important part of the labour input. Preliminary data for 1973 relating to occupiers and their wives, together with published data on employees who are members of the occupier's family, suggest that roughly two-thirds of the total labour input on farms in the region comes from occupiers and family labour.

Total employees in agriculture fell by an average of 2½ per cent per annum during the 1950s, by about 8 per cent per annum from 1961 to 1966, and by 3½ per cent per annum since then. These rates of change are very close to those experienced in Scotland as a whole over the same periods, although the rate of decline of regular full time workers has been faster in the Highlands than in Scotland as a whole.

The employment figures derived from the agricultural statistics are not easy to reconcile with those obtained from the Census reports. One might, for example, be tempted to infer that the differences solely reflect the fact that self-employed farmers and crofters are included in the Census data but not in the data derived from the agricultural returns. However, a further examination of the data suggests that the Census information may understate the total numbers employed in agriculture and horticulture to the

4 Census 1971, Scotland. Second Preliminary Report, Edinburgh. HMSO 1972.

Table 3-2. Rural Employment 1961, 1966 and 1971

	1961	*1966*	*1971*
Total Population, Crofting Counties	277,948	(274,170)	282,966
Total in Employment,[a]			
Crofting Counties	107,110	105,090	107,500
Employment in Landward Areas[b]	66,620	n.a.	63,890
Employment in Agriculture, Forestry			
and Fishing[c]	21,640	19,270	14,590
Of which — Agriculture & Horticulture	15,460	13,180	10,650
— Forestry	2,310	2,130	2,070
— Land & Estate Management	1,830	1,670	d.

Notes:
a Total in Employment: Industry and Status Tables.
b Excluding Large and Small Burghs.
c SIC 'O' Estimates subject to sampling error and bias — see source for details. Includes self-employed.
d Omitted from 1971 Census.

Sources: Census 1961, Scotland. HMSO (1966)
Sample Census 1966, Scotland. HMSO (1968)
Census 1971, Scotland. Preliminary Parish Tables.

extent that wives of crofters and farmers worked regularly on the farm.[5] The extent of this understatement might have been between 2,000 and 3,000 in the 1960s.[6]

Much of the problem in interpreting the data is associated with the part-time nature of many crofts and farms in the region. Thus many crofters who have an occupation other than farming, such as weaving, fishing, labouring, may be classified in the census as employed in these sectors. There is unfortunately very little data on the extent and nature of this 'occupational pluralism', although it is clearly of considerable importance for the economy of the region.[7]

The Crofters Commission Annual Report for 1972 notes that there were 18,320 crofts entered in the Commission's Register at 21 December 1972.

5 If one assumes that casual and seasonal labour, as recorded in the Agricultural Statistics, would probably not be counted in the Census figures, then self-employment in agriculture and horticulture would have fallen from 5,364 in 1961 to 5,194 in 1971. However an examination of the occupier data derived from agricultural returns suggests a higher number of full-time, part-time and casual occupiers than this. An analysis of the sex distribution in the two sets of data clearly indicates that wives employed on farm work tend not to be recorded as such in the Census data. In 1971, for example, the Census Industry and Status tables show a total of 1,410 women employed in agriculture and horticulture. These figures include self-employed. The agricultural statistics in 1971 gave a total of 1,755 women employed, of whom 139 were casually or seasonally employed. The latter exclude self-employed and farmers' wives.

6 This also implies that female participation rates for the region are understated.

7 Several attempts are now being made to rectify this shortcoming, one such being a small study recently commissioned by the HIDB and being carried out by the University of Aberdeen.

Table 3-3. Employed Labour in Agriculture — Crofting Counties 1951 to 1974

	1951	1961	1963	1966	1971[a]	1973[a]	1974[b]	Average Annual Percentage Change 1961-66	1966-73
Regular Workers	12,280	10,096	8,870	7,038	5,456	5,516	5,356	— 7.5%	— 3.5%
Full-time	n.a.	8,636	7,721	6,098	4,100	3,889	3,704	— 7.0%	— 6.5%
Part-time	n.a.	1,460	1,149	940	1,356	1,627	1,652	— 9.0%	+ 8.0%
Casual & Seasonal Workers	2,535	1,460	1,026	882	828	711	701	— 10.5%	— 3.0%
Total Employed Labour	*14,815*	*11,556*	*9,896*	*7,920*	*6284*	*6,227*	*6,057*	*— 8.0%*	*— 3.5%*

Notes:

a Adjusted to take account of employed labour on 'insignificant holdings' as at June 1970 assuming that the labour force on these units remained constant for 1971 and 1973. This ensures the comparability of the series.

b Estimated on the basis of changes recorded on holdings of 40 SMDs or more between June 1973 and June 1974.

Source: DAFS Agricultural Statistics 1951-1974. Excludes labour employed by agricultural contractors who do not operate that contracting business through a farm business.

Table 3-4. Employed Labour in Agriculture — Scotland 1951 to 1973

	1951	*1961*	*1963*	*1966*	*1971*[a]	*1973*[a]	Average Annual Percentage Change *1961-66*	*1966-73*
Regular Workers	87,710	73,248	66,280	52,966	42,486	40,906	— 6.3%	— 3.0%
Full time	n.a.	65,634	59,633	47,442	37,159	35,220	— 6.3%	— 4.2%
Part time	n.a.	7,614	6,647	5,524	5,327	5,687	— 6.3%	+ 0.4%
Casual & Seasonal Workers	16,390	8,921	6,592	5,329	4,811	4,193	— 9.8%	— 3.4%
Total Employed Labour	*104,100*	*82,169*	*72,872*	*58.295*	*47,297*	*45,099*	— *6.3%*	— *3.6%*

Note:
a The Scottish figures for 1971 and 1973 have not been adjusted to take account of employment on 'insignificant' holdings as the differences at the Scottish level are very small.

Source: See Table 3-3.

There were, however, only 15,443 'working units', or units where crofters made separate agricultural returns.[8] Of these, some 7,562 units were classified as under 26 SMDs (Standard man-days) and only 543 were classified as over 275 SMDs.[9] Most of the 15,443 crofts classified as working units are thus very definitely part-time or spare-time agricultural units. The precise extent of multiple tenancies of crofting subjects is not known, although the DAFS occupier data for 1973 suggest that it is considerable. If correct, this indicates that 'occupational pluralism' may now be less extensive than may be supposed from an examination of the data on crofting units, since many registered crofters must be either retired or in full-time employment outside farming (but retaining the croft house), having sub-let (formally or informally) their agricultural rights to others. A relatively small number of crofters, therefore, probably farm larger acreages than the data on size of holdings would suggest, and more crofters than might be supposed are solely employed in agriculture.

In Chapter 1 we suggested that agriculture now accounted for roughly 10 per cent of the occupied population of the region — or roughly 11,000 individuals on a full time equivalent basis.[10] Although this figure agrees closely with the census data and with a calculation based on the theoretical labour requirement of Highland agriculture (SMDs), it is clear from the above discussion that the numbers of individuals who receive at least part of their income from agricultural activities is considerably greater than this — possibly between 16,000 and 18,000.

Productivity Changes in Highland Agriculture

An assessment of productivity changes in agriculture is fraught with theoretical and practical difficulties. Ideally it is desirable to have indices showing changes in the (real) output of agriculture over time and changes in all the (real) inputs used in the same period. More commonly it is found that changes in 'output per man' are used as an imperfect indicator of labour productivity and that even then formidable problems arise in calculating such an index.

In the case of the Highlands, the available data for the past 20 years are not adequate to provide a reliable comparison with indices of limited validity calculated for Scotland as a whole. What follows is an attempt to see whether the relevant information can be presented in a form which suggests broad conclusions on recent changes in the productivity of Highland agriculture — both absolutely and in relation to Scotland as a whole. The discussion is in three sections: (i) an attempt to measure changes in

8 There are in addition some 1,900 'eligible occupiers' who occupy holdings of 'like economic status' to crofts.

9 See also Chapter 1.

10 Strictly speaking 11,000 man-years.

output per man; (ii) a consideration of data showing trends in theoretical labour requirements and actual labour input; and (iii) a consideration of inputs other than labour.

Output per man

The broad trends in Scotland in the period under review (1951/2 to 1971/2) may be summed up as follows: the gross output[11] of Scottish agriculture (measured at constant prices) rose by about 54 per cent in the period, while the labour input (farmers and farmworkers) fell by about 44 per cent. This implies that real output per man in Scottish agriculture nearly trebled, rising by around 175 per cent. No comparable figure can be calculated for the Highlands as the region's output at constant prices cannot be reliably estimated from existing data and an index of labour input in Highland agriculture comparable to that used above for Scotland is also unavailable. Less satisfactory information supplemented by qualitative comment needs to be used.

Using current prices instead of constant prices and data on the regularly employed male labour force only, it would seem that output per man (at current prices) rose slightly more quickly in the Crofting Counties than in Scotland. When our knowledge of relative price movements and the composition of the total labour force are taken into account,[12] however, it seems likely that this difference should *not* be taken to mean that real output per man increased more in the Highlands in this period. The analysis of theoretical and estimated labour input given below suggests the contrary; labour productivity increased faster in Scotland than it did in the Highlands, although relative changes in yields may reduce the difference substantially.[13] Probably the most reliable conclusion would be that labour productivity has increased at a slightly slower rate in the Highlands than in Scotland as a whole. This broad conclusion may well conceal inter-regional differences which would be difficult to detect from the available data.

Standard Man-Days (SMD)/Labour Comparisons

Standard Man-days are a measure of labour input into the various farm enterprises. They are derived from acreage data for crops, grass, etc and number of livestock of different types, ages and categories by applying

11 See also Chapter 1.

12 Especially the greater importance of self-employment which almost certainly declined at a slower rate than did the employed labour force in the Highlands.

13 See also Chapter 1, Table 1-5, and Chapter 2, Table 2-4 and comments. However, available data on yields is restricted to crops and store livestock are a more important component of Highland agricultural output. It is impossible to assess changes in physical productivity in this sector with any reliability. We do not, for example, know what changes have taken place in the average weight of store cattle or sheep 'exported' from the region: cf the discussion in Chapter 2 pp 38-42.

Table 3-5. Output per Man Crofting Counties and Scotland

		Crofting Counties				Scotland			
		1951/52[a]	*1961*	*1971*[b]	*1973*	*1951*[a]	*1961*	*1971*[b]	*1973*
Gross Output, Current Prices	£m	17.5	24.18[b]	37.51	44.23	146.0	213.58[c]	340.44	357.59
Net Output, Current Prices	£m	NA	10.71[d]	17.67	NA	NA	94.79[d]	166.92	NA
Theoretical Labour Input—Man-years ('000)		13.7	13.5	11.8	11.2	90.0	92.5	83.0	85.4
Regular Labour—Men '000		12.3	10.1	5.5	5.5	87.7	73.2	42.5	41.3
Productivity Measures									
Gross Output/Man Year Current Prices	£	1280	1790	3180	3950	1625	2210	4102	4180
Gross Output/Man Current Prices	£	1420	2390	6820	8050	1665	2800	8010	8550
Net Output/Man Year Current Prices	£	NA	795	1497	NA	NA	1025	2011	NA
Net Output/Man Current Prices	£	NA	1060	3212	NA	NA	1295	3928	NA

Notes:

a SAE Vol V, 1954.

b SAE Vol XXV, 1975.

c Revised figures. See SAE Vol XXV, 1975.

d Original figure. See SAE Vol XV, 1965.

standard coefficients. These coefficients are changed fairly frequently (about three times per decade recently) in order to reflect changing theoretical labour requirements resulting from technological changes.

A method of assessing comparative labour efficiency on farms by comparing the calculated SMDs with actual labour input has been suggested by various writers.[14] Similarly, it ought to be possible to compare regional labour data with calculated SMDs over time in order to gauge changes in relative labour efficiency. Such time series comparisons are complicated by changes in SMD coefficients which themselves reflect productivity changes. It is therefore necessary to calculate SMDs for the time series using a constant series of SMD coefficients. The most serious problems with this method are, firstly, the difficulty of compiling a time series of *actual* labour input; secondly, the possibility that SMD coefficients may be based on unreliable data; thirdly, since yield changes are not taken into account in such calculations, an important element in the measurement of productivity is being ignored.

Table 3-6. Standard Man-Days, Crofting Counties and Scotland Constant Coefficients ('000)[a]

	1951	1961	1963	1966	1971	1973
Crofting Counties	3,427.4	3,372.0	3,242.9	3,221.2	2,948.3	2,790.0
Scotland	22,522.8	23,074.7	21,406.0	20,820.4	20,752.8	21,325.7
Crofting Counties as a % of Scotland	15.2	14.6	15.2	15.5	14.2	13.1

Note:
a 1968 coefficients were used.

Source: Coefficients supplied by DAFS and applied to the various enterprise data given in the DAFS Agricultural Statistics.

Table 3-7. Theoretical Labour Requirement (constant productivity) Full-time Equivalent at 250 SMDs per man

	1951	1961	1963	1966	1971	1973	*1951-1973 net change*
Crofting Counties	13,700	13,500	13,000	12,900	11,800	11,150	
Change		— 200	— 500	— 100	— 1,100	— 650	— 2,550
Scotland	90,000	92,500	85,900	83,500	83,000	85,400	
Change		+ 2,500	— 6,600	— 2,400	— 500	+ 2,400	— 4,600

Source: Derived from Table 3-6.

14 For example, by Blagburn (1961). Average SMDs per acre for given farm types in a district can thus be compared with actual labour input on an individual farm in order to assess the relative efficiency of that unit. *Blagburn, C H,* Farm Planning and Management, Longmans 1961.

Table 3-7 suggests that changes in the relative importance of different farming enterprises would have led to a lower requirement for labour on farms in 1973 than in 1951, irrespective of technological and other changes. In the Crofting Counties the drop in theoretical labour required was of the order of 2,550, whilst in Scotland it was of the order of 4,600. Reference to Table 3-3 shows that in fact the number of regular farm workers in the Crofting Counties fell by about 6,800 between 1951 and 1973, whilst total employed labour in agriculture fell by 8,588. From these figures, and applying a weight of one-third to changes in casual and seasonal labour, it thus seems likely that productivity changes accounted for the loss of some 4,800 full-time jobs or their equivalent over this period in the Crofting Counties. This in turn suggests an increase in real output per man of about 61 per cent *before taking account of yield changes.*

Figures in Table 3-4 for the whole of Scotland show a fall of 46,804 in the number of regular workers and a fall of 59,001 in total workers between 1951 and 1973. Under the same assumptions, productivity changes thus accounted for the loss of some 45,300 full-time jobs or their equivalent over this period. Again this suggests an increase in real output per man of around 100 per cent before taking account of yield changes. This analysis suggests that productivity, ignoring yield changes, changed somewhat faster in Scotland as a whole over this period than in the Crofting Counties. But yield increases for crops suggest that the real changes in productivity in the Crofting Counties and Scotland may be closer, although a final conclusion is difficult because of the problems of assessing real productivity changes in the livestock sector.[15] It also suggests the crucial importance of yield and production increases in achieving productivity changes in agriculture. Given the earlier estimate that Gross Output per man at constant prices in Scotland increased by 175 per cent between 1951 and 1971, the above analysis suggests that a high proportion of this was associated with the augmentation of output by yield increases.

Input-Output Relationships

The most important agricultural inputs other than labour are feed, seeds, imported livestock, fertilisers and machinery expenses including fuel and oil. Table 3-8 gives some data which allow the computation of input/output ratios for Scotland and the Crofting Counties in 1961/62 and 1971/72.

The data suggest that requirements of purchased inputs per unit of output were higher for the Crofting Counties than for Scotland in both 1961/2 and 1971/2. One of the principal reasons for this was relatively high machinery expenses in the Crofting Counties. Despite the fact that the Crofting Counties produced 13 per cent of the value of Scottish output of livestock and livestock products in 1961/2, purchased feedingstuffs

15 See note 13 above.

Table 3-8. Inputs and Outputs in agriculture: Scotland and the Crofting Counties

	Scotland		*Crofting Counties*	
	1961/2	*1971/2*	*1961/2*	*1971/2*
Total Inputs £'000[a]	111,225	173,520	12,684	19,840
Gross Output £'000[a]	186,093	340,441	19,429	37,510
Input/Output ratio	0.598	0.510	0.652	0.529

Note:
a Figures are in current prices.

Sources: MacKenzie A M, SAE Vol XV, 1965.
MacKenzie A M, Martin P C and Scarlett E R, SAE Vol XXV, 1975.

accounted for only 9.2 per cent of the Scottish total. Purchases of fertilisers and lime accounted for only 14 per cent of inputs for the Crofting Counties, but 17.3 per cent of inputs for Scotland in that year. In 1971/2 the Crofting Counties produced 10.3 per cent of Scottish output of livestock and livestock products and purchased under 7 per cent of feedingstuffs.[16] Fertilisers and lime accounted for 21 per cent of inputs in Scotland and about 18 per cent for the Crofting Counties in that year.

Prima facie the data suggest an overall improvement in the efficiency of input utilisation in both Scotland and the Crofting Counties, although relative price changes could invalidate this conclusion. For example, the ratio of meat prices to grain prices appears to have widened between 1961 and 1971[17] although price data are not comprehensive enough to justify firm conclusions as to the precise quantitative effects of this.

Changes in Fertiliser Use

As Table 3-9 shows, the level of nitrogenous fertiliser use in the Crofting Counties is lower than their contribution to Scottish Gross Output and this reflects the relative importance of extensive grassland and moor management systems (as opposed to intensive cropping) in the region. There has however been an increasing utilisation of nitrogenous fertilisers in the region over recent years.

16 The somewhat lower proportion of purchased feedstuffs in the Crofting Counties is probably partly due to the lesser importance of dairying, pigs and poultry in the region compared with Scotland. It also seems probable that retention of home grown feedingstuffs (not included in input data) may be relatively more important in the region. The output proportions given relate to *total* output of livestock and livestock products so that hill livestock and other non-capital production grants associated with livestock would not be included. See also Table 1-3.

17 The average monthly price of Barley increased by 127 per cent, Maize by 145 per cent and Linseed Cake by 140 per cent between 1961 and 1971. Average weaned calf prices increased by 200 per cent, while fat cattle and fat sheep prices increased by over 200 per cent (last week in September 1961-1971).

Table 3-9. Fertiliser deliveries, Crofting Counties and Scotland: Average of two year periods, Equivalent Weights of Nitrogen in tons per annum

	1952-54	*1961-63*	*1966-68*	*1971-73*
Crofting Counties	1,837	4,768	7,235	10,392
Scotland	31,117	61,191	89,394	122,760
CC as a % of Scotland	5.9%	7.8%	8.0%	8.5%

Source: Derived from F H W Green. Changes in Artificial Drainage, Fertilisers and Climate in Scotland. Journal of Environmental Management (1974) 2, Table 2.

Table 3-10. Machinery on Farms in Relation to Output, Crofting Counties and Scotland

	Crofting Counties as a % of Scottish Totals			
	1956	*1964*	*1967*	*1971*
General				
Tractors — all types	14.4	17.3	18.4	18.6
Gross Output [a]	*12.0*	*11.3*	*11.0*	*11.0*
Cereals				
Corn/Seed drills	6.9	9.2	10.3	10.3
Combined drills	8.6	9.8	10.4	11.0
Binders	14.2	18.4	21.7	28.8
Combine harvesters	2.8	5.4	6.8	6.4
Cereal Acreage	*12.2*	*11.4*	*10.2*	*9.0*
Roots				
Root drills	12.7	12.9	14.0	15.2
Root Acreage [b]	*12.7*	*12.6*	*12.7*	*11.4*
Potatoes				
Potato planters	11.6	12.6	13.2	14.0
Potato spinners	15.7	17.9	19.7	21.8
Potato elevators etc	15.5	14.2	14.8	14.7
Potato harvesters	11.0	8.5	7.4	7.8
Potato machinery	15.1	16.0	17.0	18.1
Potato Acreage	*8.7*	*7.3*	*7.2*	*6.2*
Grass				
Mowers	17.1	18.7	19.9	21.1
Grass for Mowing Acreage	—	*15.7*	*16.5*	*16.5*
Milk				
Milking Machines	—	6.8 [d]	8.4	8.3
Dairy Cows in Milk	*9.8*	*7.8*	*7.5*	*6.9*
Fertilisers				
Fertiliser distributors	12.1	16.3	—	20.4
Fertiliser Utilisation [b]	*5.9*	*7.8*	*8.0*	*8.5*

Notes:

a Refers to 1951, 1961 and 1971 (sic) respectively.

b Mangolds not included.

c Refers to 1952/54, 1961/63, 1966/68, and 1971/73 data for Nitrogen given in Table 3-9 above.

d In 1964 milking machines were not enumerated on a basis comparable to that adopted in 1967 and 1971.

Sources: Machinery data from DAFS Machinery Census; Physical Output/Acreage data from DAFS Returns.

Changes in Machinery Utilisation

Table 3-10 shows that the proportion of various machines relative to the output associated with these machines is higher in the Crofting Counties than in Scotland and suggests that the efficiency of machinery use in the region may be relatively low.

Whilst the proportion of older and smaller machines is probably higher in the Crofting Counties, thereby modifying the strength of this conclusion, data on machinery expenses (detailed in Table 3-11) tends to confirm its general validity.

Table 3-11. Machinery expenses, Crofting Counties and Scotland 1961/2 and 1971/2 (Figures in current prices)

	Scotland		Crofting Counties	
	1961/2 £'000	*1971/2* £'000	*1961/2* £'000	*1971/2* £'000
Machinery Costs	29,648	49,130	4,435	8,820
Total Inputs[a]	111,225	173,520	12,684	19,840
Machinery costs as a proportion of all inputs	26.6%	28.4%	35.0%	44.5%

Note:
a As defined, excludes labour, interest and rent.

Source: MacKenzie A M (1965) for 1961/2.
MacKenzie A M, Martin P C and Scarlett E R (1975) for 1971/2.

Not only is the proportionate cost of machinery much higher in the Crofting Counties in both 1961/2 and 1971/2 but the increase in machinery costs appears to have been much faster in the Crofting Counties over this period. What appears to be a less efficient use of machinery is no doubt related to the structure and type of farming and crofting in the region, as well as to the higher costs of repairs and fuel due to location and geography. A long term strategy for improving the viability of agriculture in the region would have to consider measures designed to encourage the more intensive use of fewer machines and to reduce any cost disadvantages due to location factors. In this connection, the establishment of producer groups to increase winter fodder production would be an obvious way to reduce the burden of machinery costs and at the same time improve the economics of livestock rearing in the area.

Employment and Productivity in Highland Forestry

Forestry employment in the region accounts for just over two per cent of total employment. Table 3-2 shows total employment at 2,070 for 1971 and the figure for 1974 is thought to be very close to this. Although relatively small in absolute terms, in terms of its contribution to overall employment forestry employment is about four times as important to the Highlands and Islands as it is to the UK as a whole, and the proportion of all State planting which is carried out in the region has been steadily increasing.[18]

Direct employment by the Forestry Commission in the Highlands and Islands amounted to 1,123 in May 1973, which may be compared with a figure of 1,779 for September 1963 — a decline of some 37 per cent. Such direct comparisons are however misleading since the Commission employ contractors in their own forests and timber merchants, who sometimes buy blocks of standing timber, also employ their own men for felling.

With forestry employment declining, and both planting and production increasing since the war, it is evident that physical labour productivity has also increased rapidly. However, because of the importance of new planting, it is particularly difficult to prepare productivity estimates which can in any sense be compared to those for agriculture. Accepting the estimate of gross output given in Table 2-2,[19] it would appear that gross output per man employed in forestry in 1971/2 was some £3,950 including the value of the growth of standing timber, compared to about £3,200 in agriculture.

Table 3-12. Forestry Employment. Scotland and Crofting Counties

	1951	*1961*	*1966*	*1973E*
Scotland	7,908	6,800	6,760	n.a.
Crofting Counties	2,361	2,290	1,900	2,150

Sources: Censes of Population 1951, 1961, 1966. (Occupation by Status tables). An estimate for 1973 based on Forestry Commission data and Aberdeen University Survey of Private Woodlands.

The creation of employment opportunities in forestry is closely related to the planting and production programmes of the private and public sector. Planting programmes of the Forestry Commission are fixed for up to five years ahead subject to the availability of land. Production programmes depend largely on the age structure of forests, although there is considerable flexibility in deciding the age at which felling should commence. Thinning programmes also have considerable flexibility. Within forests, however, the age structure is often more imbalanced than at the national level and the maintenance of a stable employment base for local labour requires a complex balancing between levels of planting, thinning and felling. The following table, which gives figures for the Loch Awe Forestry District, illustrates this point.

18 See also Chapter 2.

19 But see the reservations and explanations in the text p 46 and n.22.

Table 3-13. Forestry Commission Planting and Production Programmes and Employment Levels

	1970/71	*1971/72*	*1972/73*
Area Planted (ha)	1,020	1,630	1,370
Vol Thinned (m^3)	5,200	19,600	10,600
Vol Felled (m^3)	20,500	7,900	13,700
Employment	91	101	89

Source: Birchmore M J and McDonagh P A. Unpublished Report to the Highlands and Islands Development Board on The Employment Generating Effect of Primary Forestry Investment in a District of Argyllshire.
Figures are from the Forestry Commission (Loch Awe).

Factors affecting Agricultural Productivity and Change

Whilst the rate of change in agricultural productivity is quite clearly dependent upon a complex series of social, geographic, economic and institutional factors, some of which are discussed in later chapters, within a given geographical, institutional and social framework productivity will be mainly influenced by two inter-related factors, namely the level of capital investment and the rate of adoption of new techniques. This section is descriptive, rather than analytical, and will concentrate on a discussion of the capital resources of Highland Agriculture.

Capital

Data relating to capital investment in agriculture are not readily available on a regional basis. Scottish figures (also recognised to be inadequate for many analytical purposes[20]) are largely built up from the sample of farms whose accounts are analysed by the three Scottish Colleges, and which include farms within the Crofting Counties. The data so derived have been used to derive a very rough estimate of total capital invested in Highland agriculture. The distribution of Standard Man Days in 1969 was used to allocate to the Crofting Counties its share of Scottish capital investment by farm type.[21]

On this basis, the total capital employed in Highland agriculture around 1969 is estimated at £148 million, of which about £38 million would be in the form of 'Tenant's Capital' and some £110 million in the form of 'Landlord's Capital' (land and buildings).

This indicates that the Crofting Counties accounted for about 14.6 per cent of Landlord's Capital and 12.8 per cent of Tenant's Capital in 1969 as compared with 13.1 per cent of all Standard Man Days in Scotland as a

20 cf Stewart I M T, Capital in Scottish Agriculture, SAE Vol XV, 1965.

21 SMDs have been used rather than acreage because it is felt that this measure gives a more accurate picture of the likely distribution of capital employed.

Table 3-14. Estimated Capital Employed in Agriculture: Scotland and the Crofting Counties Circa 1969

	Estimated Capital Employed in £m			
	Scotland		*Crofting Counties*	
Farm Type	*Landlord's Capital*[a]	*Tenant's Capital*[b]	*Landlord's Capital*[a]	*Tenant's Capital*[b]
Hill Sheep	66.4	13.1	24.0	4.7
Upland	121.7	30.5	28.8	7.2
Rearing + Arable	114.3	45.7	12.8	5.1
Rearing + Int. Livestock	16.7	7.5	1.2	0.5
Arable rearing & feeding	39.7	20.4	3.4	1.8
Cropping	133.2	53.2	5.2	2.1
Dairying	163.6	79.0	9.8	4.7
Other Farm Types[c]	97.0	46.1	24.9	11.8
Total	752.6	295.5	110.1	37.9[d]

Notes:
a 1967-68.
b 1968-69.
c Intensive farms and part and spare time farms.
d Of which about 66 per cent would be investment in Livestock and 18 per cent in Machinery. The proportion of investment in machinery rises on arable systems and is lowest on Hill Sheep and Upland systems.

Sources: McEwan L V, Capital in Scottish Agriculture, SAE Vol XXI — 1971 gives data for Scotland — see also notes in original source.
Crofting Counties estimated from Scottish data on the basis of the proportion of SMDs in each Farm Type.

whole. Whilst these estimates therefore seem *a priori* reasonable, it must be stressed that the method by which they have been derived necessarily precludes any analysis of differences between the averages for the Crofting Counties and Scotland.

Whilst Landlord's Capital has been included in these estimates, it is not thought that the concept of Landlord's Capital is useful in this context as it relates mainly to the value of land. Land is an asset which is fixed in supply, the market value of which depends on many factors beyond the potential agricultural return, perhaps especially so in the Crofting Counties where the predominant farm types are those exhibiting the lowest return on Landlord's Capital.[22] The valuation of Landlord's Capital given in Table 3-14 is based on market values for land, but since it reflects neither the discounted value of the agricultural net product of the land, nor the true opportunity cost of land, nor the potential level of asset backing for agricultural loans,[23] nor

22 cf McEwan LV (1971) Table 6.

23 This would probably be more accurately based on a conservatively calculated discounted value of agricultural net product.

the level of capital actually invested in the land historically, the economic significance of the figure is very limited. The level of investment in Tenant's Capital and fixed improvements is of much more relevance to an analysis of productivity changes.

Estimates of gross fixed capital investment by different farm types have been made for Scotland, although there are no time series or regional data available.[24] By proceeding as for the estimates of capital employed, it is possible to build up an estimate of fixed capital investment for the Crofting Counties on the basis of the Scottish data and the results are shown in Table 3-15.

Table 3-15. Estimated Gross Investment in Fixed Capital in Agriculture: Crofting Counties 1971-72

	Gross Fixed Investment in £'000 1971-72[a]			
Farm Type	*Machinery*[b]	*Buildings etc net of grants*	*Grants on Buildings etc*	*Total*
Hill Sheep	256.0	100.7	72.7	429.0
Upland	738.0	418.7	94.9	1251.6
Rearing & Arable	267.4	138.7	0.3	406.4
Rearing + Intensive Livestock	29.6	66.6	9.6	105.7
Arable rearing & feeding	42.8	10.4	—	53.1
Cropping	234.1	90.5	23.0	347.7
Dairying	388.7	286.2	113.8	788.7
Other Farm Types[c]	537.4	296.5	92.7	926.6
Total	2494.0	1408.3	407.0	4308.8

Notes:

a Based on data for Scotland given in Table 195, SAE Vol XXIV, 1974, and derived by applying the Crofting Counties share of Scottish SMDs in each farm type as at 1969.

b Refers to net investment in the sense that sales of equipment have been deducted from expenditures in arriving at the figures given.

c No data are given for other farm types in the original source. For present purposes a total fixed investment of £1 per 1969 SMD in these other farm types is assumed — this figure being lower than the average of £1.58 for all indicated farm types.

As with that relating to total capital employed, the data are built up from an analysis of a relatively small number of farm accounts and must be subject to a wide margin of error. It is however possible to carry out certain checks for accuracy. *MacKenzie* gives some regional data on capital grants paid between January 1971 and September 1972.[25] Total grants paid in the Crofting Counties over this period amounted to some £1.57 million and it

24 Scottish data for 1971-72 and 1972-73 by farm type are given in The Financial Results of Scottish Farming 1972-3, SAE Vol XXIV, 1974.

25 MacKenzie A M, SAE Vol XXIII, 1973.

may be estimated that some £1.36 million of this would be paid between June 1971 and June 1972. In addition, some £254,000 in Crofters Improvement Grants was paid in the calendar year of 1961. On this basis it would appear that the gross investment in fixed capital (buildings, fences, land improvements, roads etc) in the Crofting Counties would be close to £3.4 million in 1971-72 as compared with the estimate of £1.8 million derived in Table 3-15, which appears to be a substantial underestimate.

On the basis of Table 3-14, the *total* capital invested in agricultural machinery in the Crofting Counties would be some £6.8 million in 1969, whilst Table 3-15 shows an investment in machinery of some £2.5 million for the year 1971-72. This figure does seem somewhat high, given that it refers to 'net' investment (expenditure less sales of equipment), but there is no satisfactory method of checking it.[26]

Table 3-15 refers to fixed investment and ignores investment in livestock, which is an important element in Tenant's Capital in the Crofting Counties, and other working capital. The change in livestock numbers by category of stock between 1971 and 1972 is however known, and the average value of that stock at 1971 prices is also known. On this basis, the investment in stock between June 1971 and June 1972 is estimated at some £1 million in the Crofting Counties.[27]

Using the higher figure of £3.4 million for gross investment in fixed capital, it may thus be concluded that the level of gross investment in agriculture in the Crofting Counties was about £6.9 million in 1971-72. This represents roughly 40 per cent of value-added and 66 per cent of net farm income in that year,[28] and it seems likely that net investment (i.e. allowing for replacement of assets) was roughly half this figure.

The financing of capital investment

It seems likely that a part of this investment in the industry was financed by new borrowings since, even allowing for the element of capital grants included in the total, levels of investment of this magnitude could not be wholly financed from retained earnings.

Fragmentary evidence exists to suggest that borrowings (liabilities) tend to represent a higher proportion of assets in the Crofting Counties than elsewhere in the UK, at least for tenant farmers. The following table shows the results of some recent studies in this field:

26 The data gathered by the triennial census of agricultural machinery presents one possible source, but the categories of machine are rather broad, the time period rather long, and the value of machines consequently difficult to establish.

27 Changes in stock numbers by category from DAFS June Census 1971 and 1972. Values of different categories of stock at June 1971, DAFS Agricultural Statistics 1971 p 131.

28 Chapter 1. Value-added is estimated at some £17m for the Crofting Counties in 1971/72. Net farm income amounted to some £10.4m in the same year (net farm income being here defined as value-added less wages and salaries and gross rent paid).

Table 3-16. Liabilities as a proportion of total assets in farming

		Liabilities as a % of Total Assets	
		Owner-Occupiers	*Tenants*
England and Wales	1967/68 to 1969/70 av.[a]	22	27
Scotland	1967/68 to 1969/70 av.[a]	16	21
Caithness[b]	1969 (summer)	17	26[c]
HIDB assisted farms[d]	1966 to 1973 av.	31	40
North of Scotland College Area[e]	1967/68	21	35[c]

Notes to Sources:

a Wilson J S G, Availability of Capital and Credit to United Kingdom Agriculture, London, HMSO 1973.

b Swan W B and Senior W H, Special Report 8, Inverness 1973. Appendix V, Table 15 prepared by the North of Scotland College of Agriculture.

c Strictly speaking this figure relates to liabilities as a percentage of assets excluding 'landlord's capital' assets. See source for details.

d Derived from an analysis of the financial accounts of 67 farms assisted by the HIDB between 1966 and 1973. Although a relatively large sample, it does not purport to be representative in any way.

e Cason R G, Sources and Allocation of Capital for Investment in Agriculture. North of Scotland College of Agriculture, Economic Report No 129.

It is difficult to set much store by these calculations, or on any comparisons which can be made. The data relating to England and Wales and to Scotland which was derived by *Wilson* from the sample data collected by the Colleges in Scotland and the Agricultural Development and Advisory Service (Ministry of Agriculture, Fisheries and Food) in England and Wales is necessarily crude since the samples are of very small size and may well be unrepresentative (farmers in financial difficulties are not likely to be well represented in the samples, for example). There are also some problems in the method used for valuation of assets which may understate tenant's assets and overstate landlord's assets.[29] The other sources given tend to use different and incompatible methods of valuation.

Above all, the data given in these studies ignore structural problems in the supply of capital to the industry for new development. It seems that farmers who had received assistance from the HIDB, for example, had a higher than average level of indebtedness.[30] One reason for this is that these farmers were both expansionist in their approach and significantly

29 Wilson, for example, used the farmer's assessment of assets at current market values.

30 See Table 3-16 note d. and Chapter 4 below for further details.

younger than average — these two factors not being unrelated.[31] No fewer than 68 per cent of the farmers assisted by the Board between 1966 and 1973 were below the age of 45, whilst figures for the region indicate that only about 24 per cent of all farmers were in this age group.[32]

It is also clear that tenants have particular problems in raising loan finance for development, particularly in hill and upland areas of Scotland where the landlord's role in providing development capital has been traditionally minimal. Since security cannot normally be taken over a tenant's assets, borrowing is predominantly of a short term kind (from auctioneers, merchants and by way of bank overdraft) and the level of lending in particular areas much more dependent on the lender's judgment of the tenant as an individual, and the policy of the lenders at the time. Because many of the developments which one can envisage on hill and upland farms are of a medium or long term nature, the absence of a source of medium or long term borrowing for a significant part of the industry has almost certainly inhibited investment over the long term.

Apart from these structural problems, an important element determining the level of net investment is the level of expected returns (net of tax) from that investment. There are theoretical and practical grounds for believing that, even given long run viability, there would be underinvestment in hill and upland farming in the absence of special measures. These grounds include the expectation by farmers that returns in hill and upland farming are likely to be more uncertain than in many other farming types, a view that is associated with the more limited range of production possibilities and the longer term nature of production.[33] A further important practical point relates to the adverse tax position of the hill and upland farmer as compared with his arable counterpart vis-a-vis investment allowances, and this flows from the essentially different nature of investment on hill and upland farms. On hill sheep and upland farms a high proportion of investment is in livestock and a low proportion in machinery; the proportionate investment in machinery rises in arable systems. It can be demonstrated that the investment allowances — which apply to machinery

31 Wilson (1973) gives some general evidence in support of this point in his Tables 4 and 45. Liabilities as a proportion of net worth tended to be highest in the younger age groups of farmers — particularly in England and Wales, but also in Scotland. At the same time a higher proportion of farmers in younger age groups tended to have expansion plans.

32 cf Wagstaff in SAE (1970).

33 Whether or not such expectations are based on actual experience is another issue. Establishing whether (and the extent to which) returns to farmers in hill and upland farming have been more variable than returns to other types of farming is a more complex problem than might appear at first sight, and involves taking a view on the significance of government subsidies as a stabilising factor. At a simple level, however, the evidence of recent years would tend to indicate that gross returns and net incomes in hill and upland farming are more variable than for most other farm types. Consideration must also be given to the more technical question of whether uncertainty facing individual farmers in these areas is greater than the uncertainty to the nation in this activity.

but not to livestock — allow the arable farmer to replace more of his assets in a 'good' year at a much lower net cost than could the farmer in hill and upland situations who is in similar circumstances.[34]

Conclusions

Despite recent increases in population and employment in the Crofting Counties as a whole, in the rural areas of the region both population and employment have continued to decline. An important contributory factor has been the continuing decline in agricultural employment, which even now accounts for about one-tenth of all employment in the region and one-sixth of employment in the landward areas. Employment in other primary land using activities — forestry and game — in the region has also declined in spite of the marked increase in forestry activity referred to in Chapter Two.

There is some evidence to suggest that the fall in agricultural employment has been due in part to a change to less labour intensive forms of production and not to productivity changes alone. Although the crude data show a faster rate of increase in gross output per man at current prices in the Crofting Counties, this has probably been due largely to relative increases in prices for those commodities important to the region and there is some evidence to suggest that labour productivity — although difficult to measure — has improved in Highland agriculture at a slower rate than in Scotland. The rates of labour loss have been broadly similar, but both gross and net output per man have remained at a consistently lower level in the Highlands than in Scotland. The data indicate the importance of output-increases in achieving high rates of increase in productivity, and the slower rate of increase of real output in the Highlands could be an important reason for the less rapid increase in real output per man.

Examination of input-output relationships suggests that, in terms of purchased inputs other than labour, the Highlands are not notably different in their use of most agricultural inputs than Scotland; one exception seems to be machinery.

Analysis of capital investment in the industry is hampered by data inadequacies. Evidence exists to suggest that Highland agriculture — particularly the hill and upland sector — is probably undercapitalised and that this is one reason for the low output, low income syndrome. The comparatively high risks involved in Highland farming, the high average age of farmers and crofters, the long term nature of investments and the

34 This remains true whether a 'herd basis' or a 'trading stock basis' is used. S Kennedy worked out a simple example for us which showed that if two farmers each made a cash surplus of £5,000, one reinvesting £3,000 of this in machinery, the other £3,000 in livestock, then, assuming a tax rate of one third, the former's liability to tax would be £677 whilst the latter's would be £1,667.

lesser opportunity to write off investments against tax are contributory factors in this process. The Highland Board has been able to use its powers relating to financial assistance in a way which has helped to counter some, but not all, of these problems, and some evidence as to the impact of its activities in this and other fields is given in Chapter Four.

PART 2

The role of the Highlands and Islands Development Board in Highland land use and the principles of agricultural development policy in the Highlands

Introduction

In Part 2 we move on — in Chapter Four — to an assessment of the activities of the Highlands and Islands Development Board in the broad field of land use during its first ten years. Successes as well as failures are covered in the discussion since it is our view that open discussion of such issues can only be helpful in the formulation of future policy. Selection has been necessary because the Board has a very wide remit and has involved itself in numerous activities which have a bearing on land use; it would not have been possible to give adequate analytical treatment to all of those in a study of this kind, and our selection has sought to concentrate on the main fields of staff effort and financial commitment.

In Chapter Five we seek to draw together the main implications of the factual assessment in Part 1 and the analysis of the past experience of the Board in an attempt to restate the main principles of an agricultural development policy for the Highlands in the changing regional context. Many of these principles are already embodied in Board policy, which has had to respond to changing economic circumstances both within and beyond the region. But it is in our view important that these principles should be widely discussed and agreed both within and outside the region. Beyond this, the idea of a regional development body which has powers to intervene in *all* sectors of a regional economy is in many ways a new innovation, and an important one in the theory of development institutions generally. The way in which policies evolve in such a framework seems worthy of wider notice.

CHAPTER 4

The Role of the Board in Agriculture and Land Use

Public interest with, and State intervention in, aspects of agriculture and land use in the Highlands has a long history. Following the Act of March 1752 which annexed certain estates to the Crown following the 1745 rebellion, Commissioners were appointed to determine policy on these estates, the rents and profits from which were to be used for the comprehensive development of agriculture, fishing, communications, education (particularly the spread of the English language), manufacturing activities such as linen, and even the promotion of the idea of new settlements such as Beauly and Ullapool.[1] Over a century later, in 1884, the Royal Commission on the Condition of Crofters and Cottars in the Highlands and Islands of Scotland (the Napier Commission) reported and the Crofters' Holdings Act of 1886 set up the Crofters Commission with powers to fix and revise fair rents, to determine the amount of compensation due to any person leaving a croft, to compel land to be provided on certain conditions for the enlargement of crofter holdings and to regulate management of common rights in grazing, seaweed and peat.[2] In 1897, the Congested Districts Board was set up with responsibilities for the development of agriculture, fishing and home industries, the creation of new holdings, the assistance of migration, and the provision of certain public works such as roads, harbours and bridges.[3] Gradually these powers were eroded and/or transferred to centralised bodies such as the Board of Agriculture or local authorities.[4]

There was a brief period of active land settlement following World War I carried out under the aegis of the Board of Agriculture; the Land Settlement Acts of that period are still extant and could be reactivated at any time. However, the idea of intervention in land use by a body solely

1 Youngson (1973) p 27. These estates included, by 1770, Barrisdale, Cromarty, Lovat, Struan, Kinlochmoidart, Lochiel, Ardshiel, Callart, Lochgarry and Cluanie.

2 Collier (1953) pp 98-99. The judicial powers of the Crofters Commission were transferred to the newly formed Scottish Land Court in 1911.

3 Collier *loc cit*. Annual Reports of the Congested Districts Board.

4 In particular, the land settlement and most of the development functions of the Congested Districts Board were transferred to the Board of Agriculture in 1912.

responsible for development in the Highlands and Islands as a region was not again attempted until the establishment of the Board in 1965. In the intervening period, a series of Royal Commissions, Committees and Panels had reported on various aspects of land use and development in the Highlands, examples being the Hill Lands (North of Scotland) Commission which reported in 1956 (Cmnd 9759) and the Advisory Panel on the Highlands and Islands which reported on land use in 1964.

During the debate on the Second Reading of the Highland Development (Scotland) Bill, the Secretary of State said '. . . Land is the basic natural resource of the Highlands and any plan for economic and social development would be meaningless if proper use of land were not a part of it . . . The Highlands (Advisory) Panel made recommendations about agriculture, forestry, recreation, sport and other uses, recommendations which can only be implemented by use of the powers which we propose to give the (Highlands and Islands) Development Board . . .'[5]

The government made it clear during the debate that they intended the new Board to tackle the problems of *rural* land use among other things. The Secretary of State cited the report of the Hill Lands (North of Scotland) Commission[6] as identifying one of the main limitations on land development in the Highlands as 'the existing rights of possession and occupation in regard to all land capable of agricultural use in any form', and declared that 'with capital and progressive management these difficulties would be overcome one way or another, and one view favoured special measures to make land available to people willing to undertake developments'.[7] The removal of these limitations on land development was 'the purpose of the powers in relation to land which the Board will have'.

The most important of the Board's powers relating to land are:—

the power to acquire land by purchase, lease or excambion (Section 4(1) (a));[8]

the power to hold, manage or dispose of land (Section 4(1) (c));

the power to compulsory purchase (Section 4(1) (b));

the powers relating to surveys and the collection of information (Section 10);

the powers relating to the carrying out of business at its own hand (Section 6);

the powers of financial assistance to development schemes (Section 8).

The first strategy of the Board was set out in its First Report published in 1967. Although it was agreed that agriculture must remain an important

5 Hansard 16 March 1965, Cols 1088/1089.

6 HMSO Cmnd 9759 (1956).

7 *Op cit* Col 1083.

8 The Board was established by the Highlands and Islands Development (Scotland) Act of 1965 (hereafter called simply 'the Act').

part of the regional economy and that more could be produced from the Highlands, it was not considered likely that this increased output would be accompanied by increased employment, because of the labour saving effect of the introduction of more efficient and mechanised methods in agriculture.[9] The Board were prepared to support any projects leading to higher output from the land and greater employment, but forestry was given more emphasis in the report and was referred to as 'one of the three great hopes for rural employment and a more secure Highland economy'.[10] This prediction was not however, borne out by experience as forestry employment has at best remained static in the decade since 1965, despite increased planting rates.

During its first three years the Board's view on agriculture changed, culminating in the adoption of a formal policy document which stated:

> 'The Board recognises that it has a clear responsibility to promote, encourage and assist the development of a healthy and prosperous agriculture within the Highlands and Islands. Agricultural development in the Crofting Counties can help to support rural employment and to raise the income of those who contrive to earn their livelihood from that sector of the economy. It can make too an increasing contribution to the nation's food supplies'.[11]

These objectives were to be achieved through the exercise of the Board's own special powers, in co-operation with other bodies involved, to achieve an increase in agricultural production and the raising of 'the productivity of land and labour . . . by more efficient methods and the more intensive use of land'.

Apart from an extension of its grants and loans scheme to the agricultural industry especially 'to facilitate the adoption of more intensive methods of agriculture', the statement referred to the possible use of the Board's powers to undertake development projects at its own hand in the agricultural field and also to the preparation of 'draft plans for the comprehensive development of selected areas' which it would discuss with interested individuals and organisations and help 'to establish a procedure for implementing approved proposals in a co-ordinated fashion'.

Section 8 powers

Arising from the adoption of a formal agricultural policy, the Board was able to make much more use of its powers under Section 8 of the Act in the general fields of agriculture and horticulture. Agreement had been reached

9 Since 1966 the number of employed persons in agriculture in the Highlands and Islands has declined by nearly 2000 — but this was partly caused by a change in the structure of production. See also Chapter 3, Tables 3-3, 3-7 and comment.

10 Highlands and Islands Development Board. First Report. HIDB (1967) p 3.

11 This document was drawn up in 1968 and published in Occasional Bulletin No 2, HIDB, August 1970.

in 1969 with officials in St Andrew's House regarding the rules which would govern assistance to such projects, and these rules meant, in effect, that financial inducements of the following kind could be offered:—

1 Loans for a wide variety of purposes, including the erection or adaptation of new buildings, the purchase of plant and equipment and the provision of working capital within an agreed development programme. Interest on these loans would be charged at agreed rates which are now based on those set by the DTI for all Industrial Development Boards, including the HIDB, and the repayment period could be up to 20 years in respect of buildings or up to 10 years in other cases. Moreover — and this was an extremely important provision in terms of financing longer term land improvement and stock rearing projects — the Board could defer capital repayments and offer interest free periods (either by waiver or deferment) for up to two years. The criteria applied to the giving of loans related essentially to the technical feasibility and the rate of return on the project, with limits being set by the debt equity ratio of the business and other related factors, including an assessment of management ability.

2 A special grant could be given, although normally only to supplement loan assistance and for projects of special development value which could not proceed without such assistance. Special grant could not be given in addition to grants from other statutory sources, such as DAFS, for the same item. The amount of special grant given would not normally exceed 30 per cent of the total cost of the project and would generally be less than that, although in exceptional circumstances a grant of up to 50 per cent could be given for smaller projects.

3 As a general rule at least 50% of the project cost has to be raised from private sources, although in special cases this may be reduced to 30%.

Agricultural Policy in Practice — the Growth and Characteristics of Board Assistance to Agricultural Projects under Section 8 of the Act

By the end of 1975, the Board had a record of about 1000 enquiries from farmers and crofters in respect of their assistance for agriculture. Of these, nearly 424 went before the Board for a decision, and 38 (or just under 9 per cent) were rejected. Loans or grants were actually taken up by 360 applicants, involving Board funds of just over two million pounds.

Board finance was, of course, only one element in the financing of these projects and, although many projects would not have proceeded at the same scale without access to the type of financing which the Board is able to offer, it is important to emphasise the contributions made from other public sources, notably the Department of Agriculture and Fisheries for Scotland, and by the applicants themselves, either from savings or from commercial banks or other financial institutions. Taking cases overall, the applicants contributed something over half the total cost of the projects, with the balance coming from the Board (32.9 per cent)

Table 4-1. Board Assistance to Land Development Projects

Calendar Year	*No of Projects*	*Amounts Approved*[a] £
1966	8	22,023
1967	11	103,858
1968	16	97,124
1969	9	22,009
1970	12	121,969
1971	38	235,722
1972	86	583,188
1973	69	380,133
1974	83	559,662
1975	54	316,260
TOTAL 1966 — 1975	386	2,441,948

Note:
a Withdrawals by applicants after Board approval accounted for about 14 per cent of amounts approved shown above, and referred to 7 per cent of projects.

Source: HIDB.

and — through the statutory schemes which it administers — DAFS (13.9 per cent). It is estimated that the total investment generated by Board assisted farming projects up to the end of 1975 was some £5.2 million. Although not directly comparable, the annual average of roughly £0.8 million in 1971-73 contrasts with a gross capital investment (including stock) in Highland agriculture of some £6.9 million betwen June 1971 and June 1972.[12]

The three northern counties — the agricultural problems of which were the subject of a special Board Report commissioned in 1968[13] — received

Table 4-2. Financing of Board Projects 1966-1975[a]

	£'000	*%*
Applicant	3,505.8	53.2
HIDB	2,165.0	32.9
DAFS	916.8	13.9
	6,587.6	100.0

Note:
a Data refers to Board Approvals *minus* withdrawals.

Source: HIDB.

12 See Chapter 3 above, p 92.

13 Senior W H and Swan W B, Survey of Agriculture in Caithness, Orkney and Shetland. Special Report No 8, HIDB 1973.

Table 4-3. Distribution of Board Assistance to Agriculture and other Sectors 1966-1975.[a] Board Statistical Areas

	% of Regional (1974) Population %	*Agriculture*[b] %	*Fisheries* %	*Manufacturing* %	*Tourism* %	*Others* %	*Non-economic* %	*Total* £'000
Shetland	5.9	1.08	15.18	10.96	8.02	6.16	7.85	2,565
Orkney	5.6	12.56	12.87	5.87	2.34	3.58	6.39	1,767
Caithness	8.9	22.12	6.59	10.09	3.99	4.34	7.51	2,024
North West Sutherland	1.1	0.47	2.47	1.56	2.04	1.16	3.62	482
South East Sutherland	2.9	2.42	0.33	2.51	2.70	5.20	2.94	621
Wester Ross	2.2	0.49	7.09	1.50	8.12	3.71	3.19	1,319
Easter Ross	11.0	16.41	1.53	6.74	2.54	8.30	11.39	1,383
Inverness	16.6	13.39	0.39	18.85	14.58	29.75	10.80	3,667
Nairn[c]	2.9	0.88	—	—	0.20	—	—	34
Badenoch	2.9	1.52	0.02	1.98	9.57	2.38	3.77	1,018
Skye	2.3	3.75	3.70	1.81	5.82	3.88	3.31	1,019
Lewis and Harris	7.4	0.86	15.12	11.20	4.07	8.67	8.56	2,334
Uists and Barra	2.2	2.67	10.10	2.10	1.52	0.49	3.71	971
Lochaber and West Argyll	5.7	5.78	4.85	3.07	10.19	10.21	4.28	1,754
Argyll Islands	2.4	8.44	4.60	3.53	4.37	4.15	6.13	1,192
Oban and Lorn	4.8	3.37	3.37	2.68	10.04	3.22	4.38	1,373
Mid Argyll and Kintyre	6.0	2.71	11.16	14.00	5.42	4.07	10.43	2,305
Dunoon and Cowal	5.6	1.08	0.63	1.55	4.37	0.73	1.57	544
Clyde Islands[c]	3.7	—	—	—	0.10	—	0.17	9
HIDB Area	100.0	100.00	100.00	100.00	100.00	100.00	100.00	
Total, £'000		2,007	6,140	6,917	7,982	2,892	443	26,381

Notes:

a Unweighted total assistance (grant + loan).

b Total differs slightly from previous table due to differences in definition.

c Areas added to the HIDB area in 1975. See Authors' Note.

Source: HIDB.

36.1 per cent, Argyll received 21.2 per cent, Sutherland and Ross and Cromarty 19.5 per cent, and Inverness 22.4 per cent between 1966 and 1975. Table 4-3 shows the distribution of Board Assistance to Agriculture and to other sectors between the various statistical areas over the period 1966-1975. This indicates that Caithness has received the highest proportion of the Board's assistance to agriculture, followed by Easter Ross, Inverness, Orkney, the Argyll Islands, and Lochaber and West Argyll in that order. The five crofting areas have received relatively little agricultural assistance, indicating the difficulty experienced in applying Section 8 rules to crofting agriculture.[14]

In an area where beef and sheep production are the principal agricultural enterprises it is not surprising that most Board assistance was directed at improving the output and efficiency of these activities. This is certainly true since 1970/71 when the recently agreed terms of Board assistance became more generally known. Moreover, most of the assistance has been towards the expansion of beef breeding herds rather than sheep, mainly because calf production became profitable rather earlier than sheep pro-

Table 4-4. Analysis of Board Assistance by Type of Project[a]

Type of Project	*Board Assistance 1966-75* £'000	*% of Total*
Livestock production, all	1,344	55.0
Beef Breeding	796	32.6
Beef Fattening	66	2.7
Sheep	50	2.0
Pigs	205	8.4
Poultry	53	2.2
Dairy Cattle	174	7.1
Horticulture	129	5.3
General Farm Improvement[b]	410	16.8
Contractors	78	3.2
Marketing Schemes and Farmers' Co-operatives	318	13.0
Other	*163*	*6.7*
Total, All Projects	*2,442*	*100.0*

Notes:

a Figures relate to assistance approved by the Board.

b General farm improvement schemes are those which involve comprehensive development over a broad front and include cases where a combination of improvements have taken place, eg land reclamation combined with an increase in beef/sheep numbers, or steading alterations allied with an increase in beef/dairy numbers.

Source: HIDB.

14 Although the rates of grant under statutory schemes on crofting improvements are generally higher than those applied to improvements on non-crofting subjects, reflecting the special nature of crofting and the difficult circumstances of the crofting areas, crofters frequently face difficulty in raising the balance of finance required for a development scheme from the banks because they are unable to offer heritable security and often lack other resources which could act as security for loans.

duction following the poor years of the 1960s, but also because the terms of assistance which had been agreed were particularly appropriate for the expansion of the beef herd.

Projects involving an expansion of livestock enterprises thus accounted for 55 per cent of Board assistance, with beef breeding being the most important enterprise in this respect.

A substantial proportion of assistance has been given for the development of marketing schemes and co-operatives, and much of this has been directed towards schemes serving the Western Isles and the remoter mainland areas which have suffered in some degree from supply and price problems in the case of essential inputs and uncertain marketing conditions in the case of outputs. Assistance towards livestock marketing schemes — which has had some R & D element — is discussed below.

Horticulture accounted for just over 5 per cent of approvals, spread over 27 projects ranging from a small pilot scheme involving the specialist production of *lilium* to a larger project producing shrubs and ornamental trees in Argyll, as well as a range of intermediate projects involving production of fruit and vegetables, mainly for local markets.

The average level of assistance to land development projects over the period was approximately £6,000. Assistance of less than £2,000 was given to 29 per cent of cases, while assistance of more than £10,000 was given to only 17 per cent of cases, and much of this went to co-operatives or marketing schemes serving a large number of individual farmers. Table 4-5 gives the distribution of Board assistance classified by the type of project and level of Board assistance.

The range of financing terms which the Board has been permitted to offer has already been described, and it is interesting to note how these provisions have been used. Because of the restrictions placed on the use of grant, by far the majority of farm cases involved loans only (67 per cent) or grant and loan (21 per cent). Grants in fact totalled only 10.7 per cent of total Board assistance to land development projects and the tendency has been to use them mainly for small cases.

Loans therefore account for 89.3 per cent of Board Assistance in this field, reflecting the role of the Board *qua* financial institution rather than grant-aiding body. Analysis of the loan terms shows the most popular term to be 5 to 7 years and, since the term is decided only after close examination of forward cash flows, this reflects the lack of alternative medium term financing for certain categories of development project and/or certain categories of farmer.

Extensive use has been made of provisions involving the deferment of capital repayments and the waiver or capitalisation of interest payments for a period of one or two years, with a deferment period of two years being most common.[15] Once again, recommendations for use of these special

15 It should be noted that these provisions are now associated with the 'soft loan' terms only.

Table 4-5. Board Assistance by amount of assistance and type of project 1966-1975

Size Group	*Livestock Production*	*Horticulture*	*General Farm Improvement*[a]	*Contractors*	*Marketing Schemes & Co-ops*	*Other*	*All Projects*
£0-499	2	6	1	3	0	9	21
£500-1999	41	12	8	7	3	11	82
£2000-4999	67	8	10	8	9	7	109
£5000-9999	49	4	18	1	7	6	85
£10,000-14,999	14	2	10	1	1	2	30
£15,000-24,999	9	1	4	0	9	2	25
£25,000 +	5	0	2	0	1	0	8
No of Projects	187	33	53	20	30	37	360
Total Assistance (£'000)	1,163	114	376	65	298	149	2,165
Average £	6,219	3,454	7,094	3,250	9,933	4,027	6,014

Note:
a Includes an element of livestock production.

Source: HIDB.

provisions are based on cash flow analyses and this therefore reflects the long 'gestation' period of many farm development projects in hill and upland areas which commonly creates an adverse cash flow for a period of up to three years — especially where projects involve a build-up in breeding stock and where land improvements are being effected.

Board Assisted Farmers and Farms

Of the 310 applicants who actually took up offers of Board Assistance up to the end of 1974, some 208 involved individual farmers, the remainder being mainly co-operative and marketing schemes.[16] Nearly 70 per cent of these farmers were below the age of 45, whilst 33 per cent were below the age of 35, demonstrating that younger farmers have been more inclined to use the facilities offered by the Board.[17] A sample analysis of farmers assisted also suggested that a very high proportion of these younger farmers were married and had two or three children and, furthermore, had one or two full-time employees, the majority of whom were also married.

The number of tenant applicants has increased relatively since 1971. However, the number of cases involving tenants is still low and reflects both the absence of tenant farms in the region and the difficulties faced by tenants in financing expansion.[18] The distribution of assistance by tenure is shown below:—

Table 4-6. Analysis of Board Assistance by Tenure

	Day 1 to Dec 71	*1972*	*1973*	*1974*	*1975*
Number of cases[a]					
Owners	38 (41)	36 (45)	27 (41)	32 (45)	18 (36)
Crofters and tenants	27 (29)	32 (40)	25 (38)	26 (36)	19 (38)
Others	27 (29)	12 (15)	14 (21)	14 (19)	13 (26)
Amount of assistance[a] £'000					
Owners	195 (33)	310 (58)	133 (36)	228 (49)	102 (35)
Crofters and tenants	56 (9)	56 (25)	60 (16)	107 (23)	61 (21)
Others	338 (58)	87 (17)	173 (48)	130 (28)	129 (44)

Note:
a Figures in brackets are percentages.
Source: HIDB.

16 Of the farmers involved, some 32 could be classified as part-time occupiers insofar as they held other jobs simultaneously, ranging from postmen to part-time work on other farms.

17 Regional figures given by *Wagstaff* (SAE Vol XX 1970) suggest that only 23.8 per cent of farmers in the DAFS Highland region (not exactly coterminous with the Crofting Counties) were below the age of 45 and 7 per cent were below the age of 35. The figures for Board Assisted farms relate to all 208 individual farmers.

18 Only about 14 per cent of significant farm units were held on leasehold tenure in the Crofting Counties in 1971, as opposed to 41 per cent for Scotland as a whole, while only about 27 per cent of all land in significant farms in the region is in leasehold tenure, with 23 per cent in crofting tenure and 50 per cent or thereby in owner-occupation. See also Chapter 2, Table 2-16.

One of the problems which arose in the application of the Board's powers to give loan assistance related to security. Under the Section 8 arrangements, the Board was required to ensure that 'unless otherwise agreed by the Department in writing', each loan which they advance 'shall be secured and that the security shall be the best which the Board considers the circumstances of the particular case permit'. For owner-occupiers, the requirement that the Board take the best security available almost always implies heritable security, normally ranking second with a commercial source of credit, but this provision led to difficulties in the cases of smaller tenant farmers and crofters, who frequently had no assets outside their farming business and whose farming assets were such that it was not feasible to take a mortgage over them. Although the Board had some measure of security for loans made to crofters under Section 8(3) of the Act — which provided for transfer of the rights of the crofter and his statutory successors to compensation for permanent improvements — compensation for permanent improvements is only paid if the croft goes vacant and this would normally only occur if the crofter renounces his tenancy or if the landlord evicts for non-payment of rent. The outcome in the event of bankruptcy has fortunately never been tested. In practice, however, it was recognised by the Board that they had to take greater risks than commercial banks and as time went by the low level of losses in the agricultural sphere of the Board's activities reinforced the view that, providing a thorough examination of the projects was undertaken prior to a decision, the real risk could be kept to an acceptable level. In 1975 the Board was given delegated authority to approve loans of up to £3,000 without security providing they were reasonably satisfied as to the repayment prospects.

Whilst security problems are one reason why tenant farmers feature less prominently than owner-occupiers, smaller average size of tenant cases can also be explained by the smaller size of the units involved and the already high 'gearing' in such cases. Board assisted farmers tend to be farmers who have a larger than normal level of indebtedness. An analysis of the assets and liabilities of farmers prior to application revealed that for owner-occupiers liabilities represented 31 per cent of their assets, whereas tenants' indebtedness was closer to 40 per cent of their assets.[19]

Over 60 per cent of tenant cases involved buildings on which the balance of financing was to be found by the tenant, and this reflects the absence of landlord's capital in buildings and fixed improvements in the region.

19 Based on an analysis of financial accounts of 67 farms. The figures relate to total assets and total liabilities prior to Board assistance. Given that normal financial prudence (apart from considerations of the burden of debt servicing) would suggest absolute limits of indebtedness equal to assets, the restraint on the levels of assistance which the Board could reasonably offer to tenants becomes clear. See also Chapter 3, Table 3-17 and comment.

Bad debt

Actual and estimated bad debt on agricultural cases (including marketing schemes) at 31 March 1975 was £37,500, or about 2.2 per cent of the amounts actually advanced at that date. The average for all sectors was some 6.4 per cent of amounts advanced at 31 March 1975 and, in fact, the percentage of actual and estimated bad debt on agricultural cases has so far been the lowest of any area of the Board's work.

The Impact of Board Assistance at the Farm Level[20]

The agricultural returns for some 67 farms which had received Board assistance prior to 31 December 1972 have been analysed as part of a longer term monitoring programme. This has permitted an analysis of the changes which occurred on these farms during the period of Board assistance, and a comparison with regional trends. This comparison of physical performance has been augmented by some tentative estimates of financial performance, although work in this regard has been of only limited value so far because of delays in producing financial accounts in many parts of the region and — in most cases — by the short time period which had elapsed since the granting of Board assistance.[21]

Between 1969 and 1973 the total number of breeding cows on these 67 assisted farms increased by 115 per cent, which compares with an increase of 23 per cent in the number of breeding cows in the crofting counties. Total beef cattle numbers increased by 75 per cent on the assisted farms as compared with a 20 per cent increase in the region. Sheep numbers also increased by 14 per cent on the assisted farms compared with a small regional decline. As a consequence of these changes in stock numbers, and taking changes in other enterprises into account, it is estimated that gross production at current prices expanded by more than 40 per cent on Board assisted farms over the period 1969 to 1972 or roughly double the rate of increase in the region as a whole.

Resource utilisation also increased on the assisted farms analysed between 1969 and 1973. Somewhat contrary to original expectations, full-time labour input increased by nearly 30 per cent, compared with a regional decline of 7½ per cent. This increase in full-time employment was partly achieved by a reduction in dependence of part-time, seasonal and casual labour. The land area on assisted farms also increased somewhat through the taking in of hitherto unproductive areas, whilst drainage, reclamation and regeneration have increased the effective acreage on these farms. Finally, there has been a marked increase in the average tenant's capital

20 Most of this section is based on an internal Board report completed in 1974 entitled 'Study of the Impact of Board Assistance to Agriculture'. This report was written by the Authors and based on research work by J R A Cumming.

21 Table 4-1 shows the build up of agricultural cases.

employed on assisted farms over the period — from about £16,371 in 1969 to some £23,366 in 1973.[22] As might be expected, a large part of this increase in tenant's capital was financed by borrowings.

It was not possible to obtain precise data on the changes in value-added (or 'social income') or net farm income on these assisted farms over the period. In any event there are no annually published regional figures for net farm income or value-added in the agricultural sector. Moreover, the period of analysis was rather short and many of the projects on assisted farms had not reached full production by 1973. Nevertheless, preliminary estimates based on changes in gross output and resource utilisation, together with certain assumptions about input ratios, suggest that net farm income on Board assisted farms increased by some two or three times the estimated increase for the region as a whole between 1969 and 1972. Value-added on assisted farms is estimated to have increased by between 60 and 80 per cent over this period.

Two points require emphasis here. First, the developments examined above were in their early stages at the time the analysis was made and, because loan assistance by the Board is directed mainly towards long term investments, monitoring is required — and is planned — over a longer time period in order to establish more clearly the full effects of assistance. Second, it is impossible to prove conclusively that any desirable developments following Board help were the direct consequence of such help and would not have happened without it; comparisons with previous trends on these farms and with other non-assisted holdings provides a reasonable commonsense basis for studying the effect of assistance, but not conclusive evidence.

Conclusions on assistance to farming developments

With these two reservations, the following general conclusions can be drawn about the Board's work in relation to farm development under Section 8 of its Act.

1 The assistance given has enabled a substantial number of farms to expand output, maintain or raise agricultural incomes, and support a higher level of employment than would otherwise have been the case. Its impact has therefore been consistent with the Board's policy objectives laid down in 1968 and published in the policy statement of 1970.

2 The *form* of Board assistance (including, where approved, preferential interest rates and deferment of loan repayment) has been of particular value to younger than average farmers with heavier than average financial

22 This may be compared with the estimate of £14,272 for 1972 derived from the sample survey of Hill and Upland farms carried out by the North of Scotland College of Agriculture. The College uses full valuation for stock, whilst accounts normally undervalue stock by some 15 per cent. The figures for Board assisted farms are based on an analysis of accounts.

commitments. The selective nature of the assistance has helped to reveal a gap in the capital market for agriculture where regional development considerations are relevant.

3 The impact of Board assistance to date is at least consistent with the view that assistance of this kind can raise the economic efficiency of selected farm businesses in the Highlands to a new, higher level, and generate private and social benefits (including higher tax revenues) in excess of the real, additional cost of providing the assistance.[23]

Livestock Marketing Schemes

As already mentioned, and as Table 4-4 indicates, financial assistance to marketing schemes and to farmers' co-operatives has accounted for 13 per cent of all Section 8 assistance between 1966 and 1975. The greater part of this assistance relates to co-operative marketing schemes for calves and lambs; most of this assistance was in the form of short-term loans covering the fattening period only.[24] Because of this, although loans of over £200,000 were approved by the Board for such schemes over the period 1967 to 1972, the maximum outstanding at any time was about £65,000 (in 1971).

Interest in the marketing problems of the islands and remoter parts of the Board's area was revived in the early 1960s by the Scottish Agricultural Organisation Society (SAOS) and several schemes involving the batching of calves from different producers and direct sale to fatteners were tried during the period up to 1966. With the exception of one started in Islay by Islay Farmers Ltd in 1963, these schemes received grant-aid from the Agricultural Marketing Executive Council (AMDEC) and substantial non-cash assistance from SAOS. In 1964 a pilot scheme for direct marketing of lambs from Argyllshire was also instituted by SAOS.

For a number of reasons these schemes ran into difficulties during 1965 and 1966 when the stock rearing and fattening industries were in some economic difficulty. Feeders found difficulty in raising credit to buy calves because of general credit restraint and the auction prices for calves had fallen to a level which removed any incentive for feeders to enter such schemes. At the same time, conditions from the point of view of the calf and lamb producer were such as to render schemes which aimed at greater market stability all the more attractive. It was against this background that

23 Consideration was given to the possibility of evaluating the effects of assistance by cost-benefit analysis, but this was not practicable in view of the early stage of development of the projects. Even evaluating the costs and benefits in terms of exchequer payments and receipts presents considerable problems. However, the difference between 'hard' and 'soft' interest rates is 3 per cent per annum, and calculations made indicate that the cost of this in the period to 1973 was less than the potential tax revenues generated by the increased incomes flowing directly from the investments made.

24 This contrasts with loans for individual farm developments which were overwhelmingly medium or long term. See p 105.

SAOS proposed a system of marketing which involved the purchase of calves on a weight and grade basis by a co-operative society which would then contract with feeders to fatten the stock.

The introduction of contract feeding meant that the working capital requirements of such schemes would be considerably greater than in the case of direct sale, and it was this that led SAOS to approach the Board in 1967 for assistance to finance such a scheme for the Uists. Similar schemes were later introduced in Mull (for calves and lambs) and Islay (for lambs only). The experimental nature of these schemes was recognised from the outset and it was hoped that, by monitoring the feed and weight gain of calves, useful information could be transmitted back to producers as an aid to livestock improvement.

Over the six years between 1967 and 1973 (but excluding the 1973/4 season) the Uists and Mull calf marketing schemes handled a total of some 3,800 calves. Over the three seasons 1970/1, 1971/2 and 1972/3 the Mull and Islay sheep schemes marketed a total of about 10,000 sheep. Although the exact number of island producers participating in the schemes for every year is not known, it seems that at least 400 producers have sold calves or lambs under at least one of the schemes in one year. The calf schemes handled only weaned calves and on the basis of the above figures it is estimated that, on average, these schemes handled roughly one-third of all weaned calves sold off the Uists and Mull between 1967 and 1973. For lambs, it is estimated that on average about one quarter of all lambs sold off Mull and Islay in the period 1970/1 to 1972/3 were handled by the schemes.

The total value of sales of calves and sheep (after feeding) between 1967 and 1973 was over £380,000, of which roughly 60 per cent was accounted for by payments to island producers, the remainder being mainly composed of payments to feeders.

Taking all the schemes together for the whole period 1967-73, there was no significant trading profit or loss, the annual gains or losses of the schemes tending to cancel out over the period. When loan charges are taken into account the schemes showed an overall deficit of around £8,000 by late 1973. This deficit was more than wholly accounted for by the Uist Calf Marketing Scheme, the Islay and Mull schemes ending the period with overall surpluses. Most of the calves were in fact handled by the Uist scheme, which handled no lambs, and this highlights the fact that most of the problems over this period at least were asssociated with calves rather than with lambs.

These problems were of a technical, economic and administrative nature. Technical problems related to the largely subjective grading system, and the lack of clear data on both the potential weight-gain of different types of island calves and the appropriate feed régime for fattening these calves. Economic problems arose from the formulae adopted for price-fixing when stock were bought from producers (mainly related to prices obtaining in representative auction markets), the assessment of a reasonable price to pay to feeders for feeding cattle, the lack of incentive to feeders to feed the cattle to the advantage of the scheme once the feeding charges had been agreed, and the degree of risk being borne by the society as opposed to producers or fatteners. Administrative problems arose because producers of calves never regarded the scheme as 'their' scheme (the schemes had feeder members as well as producer members) and took little interest in the calves once they had left their hands; their objective in the circumstances was to maximise the price at which their calves were transferred to 'the scheme' rather than leave large amounts of capital tied up in calves over which they had no effective control. There was also considerable difficulty in balancing supply and demand; the 'price' for scheme calves had to be set after some auction sales had taken place and since there was no penalty for withdrawing from the scheme, or indeed any hard forward commitment of calves, wide fluctuation took place in offers to the scheme depending on the difference between auction prices and the scheme price. Finally, although a request was made by SAOS to appoint a full-time livestock officer to supervise and administer the schemes, this was not to prove possible and, partly as a result of this, the schemes suffered from complexities and plurality of control which might otherwise have been avoided.

Mainly because of these problems and the failure of those most intimately associated with the schemes to resolve them, the Board did not agree to continue to finance the schemes for contract feeding of calves after 1972/3. It has, however, sought to encourage — in close co-operation with SAOS — the development of small groups of producers in the islands who would sell their calves directly to feeding farmers, and at least one of these groups — in Uist — has been formally constituted and operated successfully for three seasons. In 1973/4 this group handled some 520 calves and in 1974/5 some 420 calves and these were placed mainly with feeders in Easter Ross.[25] Apart from advice on the pricing arrangements and help at the sales, the Board's financial involvement in this scheme to date has been small. A proportion of the calves has been regularly monitored on feeding farms by the Meat and Livestock Commission and the Board has paid for this monitoring and analysed the data in a form for discussion by producers and feeders. The Board has also helped to finance visits to Uist by feeders to see the conditions under which stock are reared, and visits to Easter Ross by Uists producers to see their cattle being fed and discuss the results of the monitoring work.

Following the 1972/3 season and the decision of the Board to stop financing the contract feeding of calves, the Uist society — Hebridean Calf Producers — ceased trading. For other reasons, the Mull society — West

25 A similar number were handled in 1975/6.

Highland Livestock Producers Ltd (which dealt in both calves and lambs) — stopped trading and two new societies were created to deal with the contract feeding of lambs — one a locally based Mull society, the other a subsidiary of West Highland Crofters and Farmers Ltd which was to obtain lambs from other parts of Argyllshire and possibly Barra. In the event, these schemes ran into difficulties in 1973/4 and later went into liquidation.

Altogether, in the period up to 1975, three of the marketing schemes assisted had gone into liquidation, and the actual and anticipated bad debt associated with these failures amounted to just over £27,000 or somewhat less than 10 per cent of the total amounts advanced.

The general objective of all of these schemes had been to reduce the effects of market fluctuations and related uncertainty which tended to become progressively more severe the more remote the location. Island producers faced particular difficulties. In the absence of co-operative or group marketing schemes, producers in the Western Isles, for example, have three main alternative ways of disposing of stock; to the itinerant dealers moving from croft to croft; through the small seasonal auction sales held locally; or through the larger auction markets on the mainland — for example at Oban, Dingwall or Inverness. If one considers four of the main criteria by which a marketing system for store livestock may be judged to be efficiency,[26] equity,[27] flexibility,[28] and comparative cost,[29] disposal through itinerant dealers tends to suffer from disadvantages in terms of efficiency and equity while offering flexibility and, probably, relatively low cost. Local auction sales also offer flexibility to the producer and allow him to compare the price offered with that offered for other stock. However, this method suffers from the possibility that buyers will be few in number, particularly when there is a buyer's market on the mainland, and because of this producers cannot be sure that the price is either 'efficient' or equitable. The large mainland markets, on the other hand, offer advantages in terms of efficiency and equity but, from the point of view of remote and island producers, suffer from the major disadvantages of lack of flexibility and high cost. For smaller producers, this alternative also tends to be physically impracticable.

Co-operative or group marketing of stock, either by means of direct sale

26 Meaning the extent to which prices accurately reflect demand for the particular stock on offer, thereby accurately signalling to producers what kind of stock it is to their best advantage to produce.

27 Equity can be considered in two ways; first, the extent to which the price is 'objectively' fair (thus relating closely to efficiency); second, the extent to which the producer can judge the fairness of the price.

28 Flexibility is valued by producers and implies the degree of opportunity to accept or reject the price offered.

29 Cost in this context means the on-costs — overt or hidden — which are implicit in the marketing system *per se*.

or by contract feeding offers theoretical advantages of efficiency, equity and cost, but flexibility is difficult to achieve except at a cost to the other advantages of the system. In practice, the advantages of efficiency tend to be difficult to achieve and, partly because of this, producers are reluctant to forego a considerable element of flexibility. Thus when prices at local markets are considered good, stock tends to be withdrawn from the schemes whilst at the same time market conditions are such that fatteners tend to be looking for stock from the scheme. When prices are poor, on the other hand, producers tend to offer more stock to the scheme at a time when fatteners find it more profitable to buy in the markets.

To this fundamental problem, and in some degree associated with it, the problem of price determination must be added. Ideally, the price of store stock should be related to the final price of the fat animal and the costs of fattening. In practice, attempts to devise a 'formula' for price determination based on these principles have been fraught with difficulty and in all of the schemes operated to date recourse has been had to a system involving the determination of an average price based on sales at various mainland markets.[30] This has left the schemes vulnerable to local price fluctuations and has reduced the possible advantages which such schemes may offer in terms of efficiency.

For these reasons, the more recent schemes have attempted to build up a much closer and more stable relationship between a relatively small number of producers and feeders in the hope that both parties will gradually accept a reduction in flexibility, which, in turn, might lead to a more efficient method of price determination. This type of scheme has had the Board's support and, because of the need for careful monitoring in the early years and the need to build up schemes of this type slowly, the Board has stated its willingness to consider assistance for the excess costs involved during the initial development period.

With contract feeding schemes, it has been difficult both to agree prices at the time stock are transferred to the scheme for fattening and to settle a reasonable charge for feeding. Although attempts were made to settle feeding costs by reference to costs of major feedstuffs, this did not prove practicable in view of the very variable performance of both calves and feeders and the wide range of possible feeding régimes. Inevitably the price settled to one approximating to the opportunity cost to the fattener of making available feed, ground and buildings for the scheme. More important than price fixing *per se*, having settled a weekly payment to fatteners there was little incentive — apart from a possible share in an uncertain bonus — to them to do the stock well since the fattener had little financial interest either in the final price or in the weight gain achieved. If such

30 The schemes commonly operate on a weight and grade system, with grading being done by a mutually acceptable grader. Auction stances on the islands usually do not have weighing facilities, so that the island prices are difficult to assess.

schemes are to be supported in future, it seems essential to base payments to feeders on weight gain with certain maxima/minima and a possible bonus on total performance. This would both cut down the risk to the scheme and give some incentive to feeders to look after the stock and feed to good effect. Such an arrangement is probably much more feasible with lambs than with calves because of the much shorter time period involved and the more certain minimum end price.

Conclusions on assistance to livestock marketing schemes

The Board have advanced nearly £300,000, much of which was in short term loans, to the various schemes which have been described above and it is difficult to measure the costs and benefits with any accuracy. The Board's loss in this field — estimated at about 10 per cent of total advances to marketing schemes — is higher than the average of 6.4 per cent over the whole range of the Board's work and substantially higher than the average of 2.2 per cent for individual farm cases. On the other hand there is evidence of a better understanding of the problems to be faced in improving the marketing of store stock from remote and island locations, of closer and more effective links between producers and feeders, and of a greater concern by alternative marketing channels to improve their services as a result of the potential competition. There is also some evidence to suggest that the schemes helped to raise overall returns to producers. For the future, assistance to marketing schemes is likely to be towards smaller groups who are willing to subject themselves to the discipline which seems essential to the success of such ventures. For example, producer members will have to accept tighter commitments to supply animals in agreed numbers, at agreed weights and grades, and which have undergone an agreed health programme; tighter pricing arrangements and a greater commitment to risk sharing; strict limitation on market purchases; and payments to feeders which provide for incentives, possibly by payments related to weight gain achieved. Beyond that there is scope for much wider efforts in the field of livestock improvement, particularly in the islands, and this is likely to involve close co-ordination of effort between the Board, the Crofters Commission, DAFS, the Agricultural Colleges, SAOS, the MLC and research organisations such as the HFRO.[31]

Special projects run by the Board

The powers given to the Board under Sections 6 and 9 of the Act allow it to run projects at its own hand. Where these projects involve the purchase or

31 The Board has supported a small heifer retention scheme in the Uists which is currently being assessed. The HFRO has recently commenced some research into the problems of cattle production in 'hill' environments which is likely to prove relevant to this whole question. Since the time of writing a working party has been set up to examine this question in depth.

lease of land, the powers given under Section 4 are also required for this purpose. These powers have been used to test the feasibility of certain categories of high risk project which, in the existing state of knowledge, were unlikely to be developed by private entrepreneurs. Thus, while Section 8 powers have been used to take action where the availability of finance was seen as the main constraint on development, the powers under Sections 6 and 9 have been used mainly in situations where a lack of knowledge was seen as the main constraint.

The main projects of this category have been the Bulb Scheme, the Shrub Scheme and the small Blueberry project.[32] Underlying these projects has been the general thesis, discussed in Chapter Two, that notwithstanding the general climatic limitations of the region there exist small areas of bio-climatic advantage which offer possibilities for the production of certain high value — mainly horticultural — crops.[33] The Bulb Scheme, which was the first of these projects, was terminated in 1972, but the Shrub Scheme is currently the subject of an expansion proposal involving a joint development between the Board and a private entrepreneur, whilst the small Blueberry project is still in a relatively early stage of assessment.

The Bulb Scheme

Bulb growing in the Hebrides was initiated by Dr A.F.R. Nisbet of the West of Scotland College of Agriculture and his colleague J.B.R. Anderson, who had undertaken field trials of daffodils, tulips and hyacinths in Tiree, Colonsay and Coll in the 1950s. In 1957, and with the support of the College, the Crofters Commission and DAFS, a co-operative society was set up — Hebridean Bulb Growers Ltd — to control bulb growing, to encourage its expansion, and to provide marketing and supply services to growers. This society was wound up in 1966 due to insolvency, and following an unsuccessful application to the newly formed HIDB for grants and loans of up to £127,900 mainly to achieve an expansion in the acreage grown.[34] Between 1957 and 1965, the number of grower members of this society had increased from 14 to 25 and the acreage grown from about 1 to 20. These growers were scattered throughout the Western Isles from Port of Ness at the north end of Lewis to the Isle of Gigha and from Achiltibuie to Tarbert on the western mainland. The scheme was started with the objective of providing a high income earning crop for crofters, but it seems that towards the end of its life many of the major growers were larger farmers and new residents.

Dean made a detailed assessment both of the reasons for the failure of

32 More recently, the Board has applied to the Secretary of State for permission to undertake a commercial deer farming project at its own hand.

33 See p 58.

34 The Society had received some £21,000 in grants and loans from the Development Commission over the period 1957 to 1965 to cover administrative expenses and other costs.

Hebridean Bulb Growers Ltd and of the future potential for bulb growing in the area.[35] He concluded that, despite the failure of the co-operative, the future of bulb growing under the right conditions seemed good. The market was expanding. Bulbs from the West had achieved a good reputation in many quarters for quality. The theoretical yield possibilities had not been convincingly disproved. Providing production was concentrated and highly organised, the prospects seemed worth exploring, especially in the light of the low incomes and unemployment prevailing in the Western Isles and the difficulty of finding viable development projects for these areas.

In 1967, a firm of Dutch consultants was appointed by the Board to investigate the possibility of reclamation and improvement of the Vallay Strand area in North Uist.[36] These consultants prepared a scheme involving the reclamation of 1,600 acres, of which 750 acres would be for bulb growing and 400 acres for an irrigation storage reservoir. The cost, then, was reckoned at about £1.4 million.

In 1969, the Board submitted a formal proposal to the Secretary of State for Scotland under Section 3(1) (b) of the Act requesting authority to proceed with the reclamation and development of the Vallay Strand as a comprehensive bulb project, for the formation of a company to acquire the assets of an existing bulb growing and marketing company in England, and to establish a production company in England.

Within this submission was a detailed costing of the proposal and a financial analysis of costs and benefits. Some attempt was also made to value social benefits in terms of increased employment and increased use of public utilities. The analysis indicated rates of return between 6½ and 9 per cent depending on the assumptions adopted. Given that the Treasury Discount Rate at that time was probably about 7 per cent, and given the difficulties of finding viable projects in the Uists, these rates of return seemed reasonable.

The rates of return were however based on yields which could not be substantiated. Although a small pilot scheme started by the Board on croft land was attempting to gather such evidence, it seems that some of the technical advisers involved were not prepared to accept evidence of bulb growth rates on 'machair' croft land as evidence of the growth rates on reclaimed land. This fundamental dilemma, together with rather poor yields experienced for bulbs grown on the pilot project, led the Board to withdraw its submission in 1971[37] and cease experimental work in 1972.

Some interesting points nevertheless emerged from the field trials and experiments carried out by the Board between 1967/8 and 1971/2. Table

35 Dean R, Bulbs from the Western Isles. A feasibility study for the HIDB. Dean was a project officer with the Board.

36 This area consists of a large tidal flat partly enclosed by islands.

37 See HIDB Annual Report 1971 para 154.

4-7 gives some results of the field trials carried out on crofting land in North Uist.

What does seem to emerge from the data is considerable variation in yield as between different years and different varieties of bulbs. This variation was also experienced on the experimental plots. The poor performance of tulips was particularly relevant to the overall economics of the

Table 4-7. Some Results of Field Trials on Machair Land in North Uist

Variety	Range of Net Yields in Field Trials 1967/68-1971/72 (%)				
	1967/8[c]	1968/9[c]	1969/70	1970/1	1971/2
Daffodil					
Quirinus	a.	111	7	—	68 b.
Carlton (D)	25	53	(12)	—	44 b.
Carlton (E)	7	85	(8)	—	72 b.
Flower Carpet	a.	33	22	—	67 b.
Mount Hood	32	37	—	50 b.	40
Geranium	40	(31)	—	41 b.	29
Golden Harvest	27	45	—	230 b.	51
Tulip					
Apeldoorn	76	77	(39)	(39)	190
Bellona	71	47	(34)	4	72
Bonanza	a.	21	(26)	(25)	64
Carlton	a.	81	(26)	3	70
Hytuna	a.	78	(16)	(5)	113
Golden Harvest	a.	70	(24)	31	90
Spalding	a.	a.	33	(7)	66
Paul Richter	39	118	(38)	(29)	a.
Orange Nassau	36	(44)	(51)	(63)	a.
Crocus					
Yellow	100	168	28	27	(103)
Pickwick	a.	80	(22)	56	36
Jeanne d'Arc	a.	72	13	(2)	1
Flower Record	a.	71	(12)	(6)	64
Peter Pan	0	50	(11)	18	(28)
Grand Maitre	50	17	25	(56)	23
Hyacinths					
Muscari	a.	25	a.	a.	a.
Mixed	a.	13	a.	a.	41
Total Cropping Area, all varieties, acres	6	23	33	21	7

Notes:

a Not recorded or not planted.

b Two year crop.

c For the first two years trials were carried out by Consultants and, as there was no drying or weighing equipment available, assessments were based on the number of trays of 'wet' bulbs lifted as compared with the number of trays of 'dry' bulbs planted. This led to some exaggeration of the yields, although the extent of this exaggeration is not precisely known. Figures in brackets represent net yield decreases.

Source: HIDB.

project; they were reckoned to be worth £260 per ton in 1969, compared with £140 per ton for daffodils and £110 per ton for crocuses.

Yield increases in experimental trials of 1970/1 were generally poor, whilst in 1971/2 they were much better — and this reflected the overall results of the field trials. The poor results in 1970/1 were considered to be due to climatic factors — namely the dry conditions obtaining in the spring and early summer. In 1971/2 a series of important experiments was commenced in order to assess the effects of shelter, irrigation, and additions of organic matter on the yields of tulip, daffodil and crocus bulbs. The growing difficulties being faced, both within and without the Board, regarding the larger project meant that these trials were under-financed and insufficient replications were made to permit detailed statistical analysis and measurement of significance. Moreover, the season of 1971/2 was held to be favourable for bulb growth and so the effects of shelter, irrigation and organic matter would in any event be less significant. Nevertheless, taken at face value, the results seemed to suggest that irrigation and shelter may well have been significant factors affecting yields.

The significance of climatic variations to the scheme has already been mentioned, and additional data on these variations is given in Table 4-8.

The differences in rainfall figures during the growing period between March and June of 1971 and 1972 are particularly marked, and the

Table 4-8. Comparisons of Climate in 1971 and 1972 — Benbecula, Uists

	Rainfall mm	*% of 1916-50 Average*	*Mean daily air temp*	*Δ1931-66 Average*	*Bright Sunshine hrs per month*	*No of Gale Days*	*Mean Hourly Wind Speed kt.*
1971							
Jan	187	156	5.6	+0.9	24.8	2	12.8
Feb	90	119	6.1	+1.2	33.6	3	12.9
Mar	91	143	6.1	+0.1	110.4	0	10.1
Apr	62	95	7.5	0.0	134.1	0	8.7
May	83	118	10.3	+0.5	166.5	0	10.7
June	63	84	11.0	—1.2	237.3	0	12.9
Mar-June	299	—	—	—	648	—	—
1972							
Jan	90	75	4.7	0.0	37.2	4	15.5
Feb	48	64	5.1	+0.2	51.9	5	15.4
Mar	60	94	6.0	0.0	134.5	4	12.8
Apr	123	190	7.4	—0.1	120.6	2	12.2
May	96	137	9.9	+0.1	157.2	0	11.9
June	135	182	10.2	—2.0	177.3	0	13.0
Mar-June	414	—	—	—	590	6	—

Source: Monthly Weather Reports of the Meteorological Office Vols 88 & 89. HMSO.

possibility of greater water stress in 1971 than in 1972 on the light, sandy machair soils receives some support from the overall figures, although it is clear that more data and analysis would be necessary to prove the hypothesis. It is also interesting to note in the light of the field trial results that the March-June rainfall in 1970 was very similar to that of 1971 at 309 mm.

One important factor to emerge is the considerable variation in climate — especially rainfall and windspeeds — from year to year. This in turn suggests that for any intensive production on machair soils of high value crops, protection from these variations in climate, either by irrigation and shelter or by other means, is likely to be very important, and this, of course, imposes additional costs on these enterprises which may not have to be met elsewhere.

It is easy to criticise the proposed scheme with hindsight. Insufficient experimentation had been carried out before the project was launched and it seems probable that the only way to carry out such experiments properly to the satisfaction of all would have been to reclaim a part of the Vallay Strand and lay on irrigation. This in itself would have been a very costly process. At the same time the Board was clearly anxious to find projects which would have a significant impact on the low incomes and unemployment in the Western Isles — and the appeal of the Bulb Scheme was understandable in this context.

The Shrub Project

The pilot shrub project at Ormsary on the western seaboard of Argyll was set up in 1970 following discussions with the West of Scotland College of Agriculture and other parties involved. The initial purpose of this project was to examine the growth rates of a wide range of shrubs in the location chosen. The project would be financed by the Board, monitored by the College of Agriculture, and would take place on a small area of rented land. Marketing of shrubs produced would take place through an established marketing outlet in the West of Scotland. Initially on ¾ acres, the site was later expanded to nearly 4 acres, and discussions are now in progress for a joint project with a private entrepreneur which will eventually expand to 25 acres on a site close to that at Ormsary.

Up to March 1975, some £22,500 had been expended on developing and running this project. While the initially experimental nature of the project, its small scale, and the lack of propagation facilities undoubtedly raised costs above those that would be expected on a commercial venture, revenues of the project up to March 1975 have been £9,600 and the value of the shrubs and other assets are valued at between £12,000 and £15,000. The evidence suggests that the growing of certain shrubs is technically feasible in favoured locations of the West Highlands and could be a viable economic proposition. As with other horticultural crops grown in these areas, however, shelter from strong winds and salt spray, together with irrigation at critical periods, seems essential. Demands on skill and expertise — in both growing and marketing — are also considerable.

Blueberries

'Blaeberries' are an indigenous wild fruit in the Highlands and Islands and trials of the commercial varieties of Blueberry — which are widely grown in the USA — were perhaps natural in this context. A pilot project was set up in 1971 on a five acre site in Easter Ross, but considerable problems of management arose and conflicts of opinion emerged between the Board's consultant — who had been one of the promoters of the project — and other sources of technical advice such as the Scottish Horticultural Research Institute. In 1973, the day-to-day management of the project was taken over by the Horticultural Section of the North of Scotland College of Agriculture and a major attempt was made to overcome the weed problem which had beset the project from its inception. Difficulties were faced in obtaining supplies of additional plants to replace those which died between 1971 and 1973, and the planted area is now somewhat less than was originally envisaged. Nevertheless, since 1973 the growth of the plants has been satisfactory and it is intended to fruit the bushes in 1976 to assess yields. Trials are also proposed which will measure the losses likely to be sustained from bird damage when the fruit is not netted. It is too early to draw conclusions from this project, although it may yet indicate a possible alternative, or supplementary, enterprise for farmers in the region.

Red Deer Farming

The idea of Red Deer farming is not new and for the past four years the Hill Farming Research Organisation and the Rowett Research Institute have been examining the technical performance and behavior of Red Deer under intensive conditions on a Hill Farm in Kincardine.[38] This research has been especially valuable in examining hind productivity (calving percentages), weight gain under hill conditions, the proportions of edible and quality meat in carcases, feed conversion efficiencies, supplementary winter feeding requirements and the like. The preliminary results of this research were published in 1974 and gave an optimistic picture of technical performance. Calving percentages of over 90 per cent seemed possible in hill conditions providing management was adequate; weight gain from hill pastures was good and conversion efficiencies excellent.

Yet considerable doubt remained as to the commercial viability of deer farming. Fencing costs under the Glensaugh system were too high to be viable at today's costs. Management input was considerable. Although the

38 cf Blaxter K L, Cunningham J M M *et al*, 'Farming the Red Deer', HMSO 1974.

prospect of reasonable rates of return from deer farming on marginal land was in sight, it would be necessary to carry out research into an appropriate commercial system of deer management. This is the purpose of the proposed project which the Board is planning to set up.

Conclusions on projects

The limited number of projects in the land use field which the Board has promoted is a reflection of the many difficulties facing this type of innovating development in the Highlands. Inevitably any realistic assessment of the impact of such projects must await their transformation into expanded commercial ventures. While this did not happen in the case of bulbs, it does seem likely to happen in the case of shrubs and there do appear to be grounds for the belief that a wider expansion — particularly in Argyll — could take place in the future. One significant advantage of this type of production is that it offers good employment opportunities — especially for female labour — in remote locations where such opportunities are difficult to find. It also provides a means of producing high value commodities from relatively small areas of ground such as may be available on a relatively large number of crofts, farms and estates in that area.

Among the lessons to be learned from the few projects already initiated is the need to establish procedures by which to select the most promising potential developments and to ensure the proper monitoring of them. At the outset there will be an experimental element in any project, but this preliminary step should be followed by an appraisal of the likely costs and benefits which, in principle, should embrace an evaluation of social as well as private costs and benefits as a guide to the level and nature of public support. For smaller developments, full-scale analysis is unlikely to be justified; in the case of major projects, the problems of carrying through such an analysis at a regional level are severe. The absence of reliable technical and economic data is a well-known difficulty; in addition the need to use appropriate discount rates and 'shadow' wage rates raises wider issues. Even if accepted values for these rates exist at the national level, these may not be appropriate at the regional level where objectives and resource availabilities and utilisation may differ. Despite all these obstacles — and perhaps because of the absence of any general agreement on such issues — it is desirable that a development board should take this kind of approach as far as is practical and should make clear its objectives and the criteria it uses. Possibly of even greater practical relevance is the need for the Board to monitor those projects which are introduced and to report regularly on their progress.

Land Use Surverys

These two policy instruments — financial assistance and projects — were complemented by a third in the form of comprehensive land use surveys which were seen as forming an essential part of the Board's policy to 'draft plans for the comprehensive development of selected areas' of the Highlands and Islands.[39] As a result of the Land Use Report of the Advisory Panel on the Highlands and Islands, and as recommended by that body when it was dissolved following the Board's establishment, the Board initiated work on detailed land capability studies on Mull and in the Strath of Kildonan shortly after its establishment. From the Board's point of view, the main question to be answered in such surveys was 'which particular use of the land will, for a given investment, produce the best return for the largest number of people.'[40] However, in determining optimal use, particular weight was to be given to productivity and employment.

The general objectives and methods adopted are described in greater detail in the Mull Report.[41] Three basic steps were involved, namely:

(a) technical surveys of land capability, which in the case of Mull were prepared by John Bibby of the Macaulay Institute for Soil Research;

(b) supporting surveys and consultations in order to carry out an economic assessment of different forms of investment which could provide employment based on land development;

(c) detailed consultations with landowners, farmers and crofters and public bodies on the conclusions drawn prior to processing detailed recommendations.

The land capability surveys were based on the classification procedures discussed more fully in Chapter 2 and Appendix 2A. A comparison with maps of existing land use revealed some 12,000 acres which were capable of improvement by cultivation or surface treatment using existing techniques.[42]

It was recognised that any assessment of the technical feasibility of improving land, or changing its use, would have to be complemented by an economic evaluation of the alternative possibilities, and the difficulties of making such an evaluation were acknowledged. Although comparisons of financial rates of return and the cost of additional jobs were made in the report, it was recognised that 'some of the main decisions relevant to a development programme might have to be taken without definitive detailed financial or economic assessment'.[43] Nevertheless, the rates of return on investment in land using activities on Mull were not seriously out of line with similar investment in other parts of the region, and since the land resources would have a low or zero opportunity cost, both forestry and

39 Occasional Bulletin No. 2, HIDB August 1970. See also Chapter 2.

40 cf First Annual Report (HIDB 1967) pp 28-29.

41 Island of Mull — Survey and Proposals for Development. Special Report No 10, 1973.

42 *op cit* p 18.

43 *loc cit.*

agricultural development were given a prominent place in the final recommendations.[44]

These recommendations related to land in both private and public hands. Publicly owned land, to the extent that it was within the control of the authorities involved, could be developed by DAFS and the Forestry Commission following their agreement with the recommendations in the report.[45] The implementation of the proposals for the private sector was recognised as being more problematic. Although the technical possibilities existed and the economic conditions could be provided with the help of the Board's powers under Section 8, it was felt that other obstacles would remain.[46] The 'attitudes and motivation of those who currently own or occupy the land' was seen as an important influence on the further development of the land resources and while many farmers and others were concerned to improve the land and lacked the means to do so 'some estates were acquired mainly for residential or sporting purposes, and land improvement is not an important aim of estate policy'.[47] Moreover, 'the piecemeal fashion in which land often becomes available to the Forestry Commission hinders the proper planning of the forest and creates an element of uncertainty about further changes in land use which has an unsettling effect on many occupiers of land'.

The fears voiced at that time have been justified by events since the reports on both Mull and the Strath of Kildonan were written, and the differences in opinion and objectives between some landowners and the Board have remained.

One view is that such differences are inevitable given the differences in objectives between the Board on the one hand and the landowners on the other, irrespective of any disagreement which may exist on facts or the interpretation of facts. What seems to be lacking is a satisfactory means of resolving these differences which is both equitable and which will give due weight to the regional development priorities of the Board (and, implicitly, the needs of the community).

A reading of the parliamentary debates at the time the Board was set up

44 The main recommendations for agriculture and forestry are summarised in paras 136-143 and 162-174 respectively. An annual programme of 100 acres of land to be reclaimed to arable standard, 500 acres to be regenerated by surface treatment, together with increased stocking and other investment was envisaged for agriculture. For forestry, a continuation of a planting rate of 1,200 acres per annum was recommended.

45 In fact by 1975 a number of the development proposals relating to publicly owned land — for example at Scoor — had been agreed with DAFS and the Forestry Commission. Commission.

46 *op cit* para 55.

47 In the observations offered to the Board on an earlier draft of the report it became clear that 'sport, and in particular deer stalking, is regarded as being of considerably higher importance relatively to agriculture and forestry than indicated in the report, and it has to be recognised that some estates will not be in favour of exploiting the indicated agricultural potential to the extent recommended'. *op cit* Appendix 6.

suggests that the powers given to the Board under Sections 4(1) (a), 4(1) (b) and 4(1) (c) were intended to provide the means for the Board to implement its land development proposals if these were being frustrated by landowners. In the event, these powers have not been put to the test.

Nevertheless, the Board has considered the acquisition of a number of estates by voluntary agreement,[48] although up until recently this course of action seemed unlikely to succeed because of the rapid escalation of land values and the inevitable lag in values placed on land by the District Valuer, who is responsible for setting the prices which the Board can offer. Moreover, although criteria have not been laid down, the Board has to justify acquisition economically, and until very recently prices being paid on the free market reflected a large number of considerations which the Board, as a public body, could not include in its own reckoning of the economics of land purchase. Among the most important of these factors were the roll over provisions relating to capital gains taxation, the death duty relief, and the favourable fiscal treatment of private forestry.

Of the four estates which have been examined by the Board in recent years with a view to possible acquisition, the first has seen five years or more of negotiation and has so far failed to reach a conclusion. The second changed hands for approximately three times the price which could have been justified by a public body. In the third case, the Board obtained permission under Section 4 to offer for the land,[49] but shortly afterwards it was sold to a private buyer. The fourth — in Mull — was the subject of an offer to purchase by the Board but in this case, although the vendors would have accepted the offer, permission to conclude under Section 4 was withheld. Even voluntary acquisition by the Board seems to be fraught with difficulties.

Compulsory Purchase powers have been considered in two cases following the breakdown of voluntary negotiations. Since powers of compulsory purchase are normally only applied following a failure of voluntary negotiations, all the problems which even voluntary negotiations pose must be faced prior to taking steps to acquire an estate compulsorily. Under the present procedures for compulsory purchase, an application of a compulsory purchase order must specify the exact purpose for which each 'parcel' of land involved is to be acquired.[50] This purpose must be clearly stated and be specific. Thus, for example, the proposed use of each field would need to be

48 These included estates in the Strath of Kildonan and in Mull, the acquisition of which would have offered the Board scope to implement some of their development proposals for these two areas.

49 The Secretary of State's approval is required for the exercise of Section 4 (1) (a) powers involving the acquisition of land by purchase, lease or excambion.

50 Section 4 (2) of the Act states that 'The Acquisition of Land (Authorisation Procedure) (Scotland) Act 1947 shall apply in relation to the compulsory purchase of land by the Board as if this Act had been in force immediately before the commencement of that Act and as if the Board were a local authority within the meaning of that Act'.

specified, presumably in terms of cropping, stocking etc. These procedures are framed in terms of local authority needs for quite different purposes in relation to precise areas of ground — schools, hospitals, roads etc — where the room for argument about the need for a facility is strictly limited and where evidence as to the respective merits of different sites can be gathered relatively easily. They are not appropriate for the acquisition of relatively large tracts of land over most of which the main use will be agriculture or forestry.

If the Board is to have the reserve powers which it needs in order to implement its comprehensive development plans for areas like Mull, then it needs a method of acquisition which does not rely on the procedures set out in the 1947 Act, but which is geared specifically to the problems of rural land.

Several possible procedures could be considered. Assuming development proposals for an area have been approved by the Board but that their implementation requires the acquisition of specific land resources, the relevant responsible democratically-elected local authority could be involved. If the local authority accepted the Board's analysis and proposals it could then undertake the acquisition of the land required for implementation. Alternatively — and going to the other extreme — the necessary powers of approval might simply be invested in the Secretary of State. A middle course which would allow full expression of the views of the local community as well as the owner concerned and the central government could be on the following lines:

(a) The process of survey and report more or less carried out in the case of Mull, with the draft report receiving wide circulation.

(b) A public hearing of objections, possibly held under the aegis of the Scottish Land Court, which has considerable experience in agricultural affairs in the region.

(c) Publication of a set of detailed final proposals taking into account any objections, and reporting on those objections which were not accepted. These would be put before the Secretary of State for his consideration.

(d) Publication of the Secretary of State's comments on the proposals.

(e) Detailed discussion with landowners and others on implementation with provision for financial inducements as appropriate. Some amendments to the Section 8 arrangements might be required to allow financial inducements to be tailored accordingly.

(f) Provision for acquisition if private landowners fail to implement the agreed programme, with objections 'in principle' disallowed.

Such procedures would ensure that the overall development proposals for an area will have been widely discussed and agreed with many private individuals and Government departments. To the extent that agreement is reached, the provision of the resources — from either public or private sources — will therefore have been accepted. It can be argued that it matters little thereafter in overall economic terms whether the resources come from public or private sources unless there are good grounds for believing either that the opportunity cost of these resources differs markedly or that the distributional implications in either case would be unacceptable.

A set of procedures of this kind would affect — and be affected by — the public acquisitions of rural land by other public bodies. As has been indicated in Chapter Two, public acquisitions of land since the War in rural areas of Scotland have been limited, with few exceptions, to purchases by the Forestry Commission. The Commission was set up as a forestry authority with the primary objectives of planting trees, producing and supplying timber, and maintaining adequate reserves of growing trees. The Commission does not have *as a primary objective* the pursuance of land use objectives as determined by regional development aims and resource availabilities. This means that conflicts can arise and, as the experience of Mull shows, a detailed land development programme can be frustrated if the piecemeal acquisition of land by the Commission referred to earlier continues. If adequate procedures are to be developed for implementing proposals for privately owned land, then similar procedures must be adopted for publicly owned land. Thus where the Commission is involved in the preparation of the overall programme for an area — as it is at present — then if the land zoned for forestry is not made available for afforestation by private owners, the acquisition by the Board would follow with subsequent resale to the Forestry Commission of those areas of land scheduled for afforestation. This would also ensure the greater co-ordination of forestry and agricultural development which is often recognised as a general weakness of the present afforestation procedures.

Conclusions

This account and discussion of the agricultural activities of the Highland Board has concentrated on financial assistance, projects and comprehensive surveys. The Board has also made many informal and several formal representations to government on a number of policy issues relating to agriculture, forestry and land use in its region and has carried out, or commissioned, a wide range of research activities which are generally detailed in the annual reports of the Board. However, the main effort has been related to the activities described in this chapter.

The powers given under Section 8 of the Act have enabled the Board to fill an important gap in the capital market in a way which has helped farmers to increase both output and income and, thereby, to maintain, or even slightly increase, employment. They have also enabled the Board to provide finance for new ventures in fields such as marketing.

Similarly, the ability of the Board to carry out projects at its own hand has been an important adjunct to its other powers and activities. Although these projects have not been without their problems, and not all can be expected to be successful, it is only by efforts such as this that new possibilities for development can be explored.

These powers and the activities related to them are not, however, adequate in themselves to secure an improvement in the utilisation of the land resources of the region. They cannot be easily used to change the age structure of farmers. Nor have they yet proved to be adequate tools for solving the problems associated with the large number of small crofts and the utilisation of common grazings which were referred to in Chapter One. Finally, they cannot solve the problem of land which is underutilised either because the landowners or occupiers of land are immune to financial incentives, or unable to provide a matching contribution from their own resources, or because their objectives are mainly related to residential or sporting uses of the land and land development for agriculture or forestry is low on their scale of priorities.

This last problem has been highlighted by the work of the Board in relation to its Land Use Surveys, where the powers of the Board to implement its comprehensive land use programmes have proved to be deficient. It can be argued that if the implementation of plans of this kind is to be more than a pious hope, then a change of procedures, possibly involving new legislation, will be necessary.

CHAPTER 5

Principles of Agricultural Development Policy in the Highlands

The Highlands as a Regional Problem

The case for a regional development agency with special policy and powers depends on there being a recognisable degree of common problems within its area and a sufficient degree of difference between these problems and those elsewhere in the country. It rests also on the view that a comprehensive approach to development in the region needs to be taken; that is, in simple terms, that what is attempted in some sectors of the regional economy should take account of, and be taken into account by, other developments.

It is not a purpose of this study to debate the wisdom of regional policies in general nor to assess the extent to which the conditions mentioned above were present in the Highlands in 1965 and are present now. But it is relevant to consider the extent to which elements in the case for a regional development policy for the Highlands and Islands must necessarily include a regional approach to agricultural development and predetermine, at least to some extent, the main features of such an agricultural development policy.

Within Britain the original concept of a regional policy, involving State incentives for economic activities in certain areas, was generally associated with proposals to encourage industrial developments in urban areas with chronically high unemployment rates. In the Highlands in the 1960s the central problem was widely considered to be depopulation;[1] while the unemployment rate was high for the region as a whole it was relatively low in most urban centres and abnormally high in several outlying areas. Depopulation was associated with the decline of employment in primary

1 'It is significant that most opinions, as we have studied and listened to them, accept that depopulation of the area is the central problem — indeed, it is almost the only common factor.' First Report, HIDB, page 2. Some commentators, however, believed there was no economic case for Highland development and that the economic solution to the 'Highland problem' was to encourage labour to leave the area. See the article by D I MacKay and N K Buxton, *Scottish Journal of Political Economy*, vol 12, 1965.

industries and the virtual absence of manufacturing industry. Unless special measures were taken, it was argued, many areas would soon reach a critically low level of population density, the continuation of basic public services would be threatened and, at best, only a semi-derelict economy would survive. The general validity of that prediction will never be tested; the prospect was sufficiently real to promote counter-measures. Theoretically, at least, many of these could have been (and some were) introduced merely as extensions of existing forms of regional assistance. Stemming depopulation depended on creating new jobs and this was what various regional policy instruments were designed to do. No doubt the view was held in some quarters that these existing instruments were adequate to deal with the Highland problem. Very probably, too, the decision to go ahead with a special authority was primarily a political judgment with strong historical and cultural undertones. But the essence of the case for a new authority did not lie so much in the arguments for providing more generous aids to the Highlands than for other assisted regions but in the view that a co-ordination of effort was required.

By the middle of the 1970s the 'regional' problems of the Highlands were rather different to what they had been ten years earlier. Even by 1971 the relative decline in population, employment and even agriculture had at least been slowed down if not halted (see Chapter One). More recently the exploitation of North Sea oil has generated new employment opportunities in several areas, especially Shetland, and the Moray Firth, and has had indirect effects elsewhere in the region. With most of the relevant economic indicators pointing in the right direction, the main regional problem is almost certainly that of unbalanced growth within the area and the aim of a regional body in the next decade will be to ensure the correct balance, geographically and structurally, within the development process that is emerging in the Highlands as a whole. Depopulation can no longer be considered to be the central problem of the Highland region in general; the fact that it is still a feature of certain rural areas within the region is a signal that a more disaggregated approach to the region's development is appropriate and that economic relationships and interaction within the Highlands must now become of central concern to an authority charged with responsibility for improving the well-being of the people of the Highlands.

The implications for regional policy of the interdependence of economic activities is a familiar theme of specialist literature and was reflected in public comment on Highland policy before and after the Board was established.[2] The extent to which a regional authority should or can institutionalise this co-ordination is not readily determined; for a variety of

2 See for instance the article by D Simpson, 'Investment Employment and Government Expenditure in the Highlands, 1951-60', *Scottish Journal of Political Economy*, Vol X, November 1963.

reasons the Board did not start by formalising its role as a co-ordinator but concentrated on 'drawing up a broad set of policies' and regarded its primary duty as inducing 'more industrial enterprises to establish themselves in the area . . .'.[3] In recent years administrative developments have moved towards more formal organised co-ordination in certain areas and the localised boom in oil-related industries has prompted more overt recognition of the interdependence of various economic activities. But the extent to which regional planning powers (including financial aid) are to be co-ordinated by or even concentrated in one authority such as the Board, is still open to change. Co-ordinating functions have grown empirically rather than schematically as a matter of principle.

The Role of Agriculture

The precise role of agriculture in all this is more complex than might be expected. Insofar as increasing efficiency in farming in the 1960s was associated with larger farms, with more capital intensive methods and with low labour inputs, then the more agricultural development appeared likely to accentuate rather than to solve the Highland problem. Insofar as aid to Highland agriculture was determined by national considerations (including the release of agricultural manpower) the less attractive such forms of assistance appeared as an instrument of a regional policy designed to halt depopulation. Insofar as income levels in Highland farming (and crofting) were low,[4] relative both to farm incomes elsewhere and to other Highland occupations, the less agricultural development seemed a suitable means for raising living standards. Put in simple terms, since the course of development in agriculture appeared to be a main cause of the Highland problem in the 1960s, it seemed absurd to look on the development of that industry as helping towards its solution.

Crucial to the debate is what is meant by the 'development' of agriculture within the Highland context. At the extremes (and equating development with some improvement in economic efficiency) it can either mean increasing output with a less than proportionate increase in resources used or reducing the resources used with a less than proportionate decrease in output; the emphasis, in short, can either be on increasing output or reducing inputs and the point of greatest advantage to the country as a whole can shift between the two extremes as various economic circumstances change. During the 1960s many specialists in agricultural policy placed the emphasis on reducing resources (especially manpower) through the enlargement of farm units. While some increase in output might be acceptable for a few products, it was argued that the main danger lay in over-production

3 Address by Robert Grieve, Chairman of the Board, to 7th Highlands and Islands Conference, organised by the STUC, November 1968.

4 See Chapter 1, p 10.

not under-production. It followed that in areas where agriculture was a relatively large part of the regional economy, the regional problem was to provide more non-agricultural jobs while the agricultural problem was to enable farming to continue to decline as a means of employment without hindering technical progress or bringing severe hardship to those engaged in the industry.

In Britain in the mid-1970s the emphasis of opinion (as expressed at least in the agricultural policies of all the main political parties) has shifted in favour of the expansion of agricultural production though disagreement no doubt still exists about what should be the pace of expansion in different sectors and what should be the level of resources and incentives used. For the Highlands the most important question arising in this debate is whether or not the production of sheep and beef cattle should be increased. Short-term instability in livestock markets has clouded the issue during the last year or so but the long run view remains that an upward secular trend in UK production of lamb and beef will be justified — assuming no disproportionate increase in resources and incentives is needed to bring this about. Just as important, perhaps, is the universally recognised need to try to avoid undue fluctuations in the numbers of breeding sheep and cows, the predominant types of livestock enterprise in the Highlands; the gradual and steady expansion of the breeding ewe flock and hill cow herd and of the winter fodder supplies they require appears to be an established objective of national agricultural policy.

The development of Highland agriculture in the near future should therefore include an increase in the output of its main traditional products — sheep and beef cattle — as a contribution to national agricultural objectives. For regional *and* national reasons, sheep production may require special attention. As earlier chapters have shown they are relatively more important in the difficult areas and are now at the centre of much development work despite having lagged in terms of technology and production over the past century. Moreover, in the context of the EEC, price trends in the future seem likely to be more favourable than for many other products.

A more difficult question is whether and when economic developments in parts of the region (eg, industry in the Moray Firth, tourism more generally) will begin to alter the local market for other farm products which up till now have only been produced in small quantities. The regional consumption of liquid milk, fresh vegetables and soft fruit will certainly rise as the total population increases and this enlargement of the local market will provide a more favourable environment for the expansion of regional production of this type of produce. In terms of Highland agriculture as a whole, however, these enterprises will play a less important part than sheep and cattle in any development of the industry in the near future.

In the period when the broad objectives of national agricultural policy have moved towards expansion, the geographical emphasis of the Highland problem has also shifted towards the more rural areas and the Board's general economic strategy has given higher priority to spreading development geographically and on getting the right kind of balance between different sectors of the economy. These elements in the situation all argue against a rapid decline in agricultural employment and support the view that an expansion of farm output sustaining a demand for manpower close to its existing level should be a desirable objective of Board policy. Where non-agricultural developments are possible and desirable then the supporting role of agriculture should be recognised and brought within a comprehensive approach to the area's development.

This approach reflects a different emphasis to that of a policy which characterises the agricultural problem in an area like the Highlands as *primarily* (or, indeed, exclusively) a problem of low incomes which cannot be mitigated by increased output but only by reducing the agricultural population. The agricultural problem over most of the Highlands must, in our opinion, be seen as part of a typical regional problem of rural areas where the maintenance of a settled community of a minimum density is at risk. What is desirable is not the achievement of a single over-riding aim (for example, high income per person left in agriculture regardless of other consequences) but an advance towards several initially compatible objectives — an increase in income, an increase in production (and productivity), and at least a slowing-down of rural depopulation. Such an approach does not deny the existence of structural problems manifested in the less efficient use of machinery and the less than optimal use of some land on small units. But it argues for a public policy to overcome these problems with the help of and by encouraging a greater and technically better labour input from those now working the land. The emphasis should be on increasing output and reducing costs through the co-ordinated and shared use of resources where present forms of tenure and farm organisation put agricultural production in the region at a disadvantage with the rest of the country. If Britain needed less and not more home-produced food, then such a policy would obviously receive little support on national economic grounds. Under present circumstances the arguments based on regional needs are reinforced by national considerations.

It should be obvious, of course, that the process of change — whether in the external situation, or in the policy approach — is gradual and reflects itself in changes of emphasis rather than stark alternatives. For instance, even with an overall increase in output, a general decline in agricultural employment in parts of the region may well continue for a time though at a slower rate without the rural population falling below a critical level. It is the directional effect of policies rather than the precise extent of their influence that is of practical relevance.

Regional Aids to Agriculture

It follows from all this that any regional aids granted to agriculture in the Highlands and Islands should have the central purpose of increasing output and not decreasing manpower. Ideally the increase in production should lead to higher levels of income and thus to the retention of manpower which might otherwise have left the industry. The aid should be linked to technological or managerial improvements which are likely to raise the economic efficiency of the industry — again without the reduction of total labour inputs. The capital investments associated with these developments should be output-raising, increasing the yields of crops (or introducing new crops) the stock-carrying capacity of the land and the productivity of the livestock; a development which simply leads to the substitution of capital for labour would be undesirable.

Within Britain's system of agricultural support in the 1960s a series of grants already existed which, in effect, provided special help to livestock farming in hill and upland areas, including the Highlands. These grants included headage payments on hill cows and hill ewes, grants for producing winter keep and various other subsidies, including special grants to crofters. While the case for such assistance was rarely defended in detail by government spokesmen, it rested in part on social or regional grounds (ie, on wishing to maintain livestock rearing as a source of employment in hill and upland areas) and partly on the view that the retention of substantial numbers of breeding livestock in this area could, in the long run, prove worthwhile economically or, at worst, constitute a strategic reserve of healthy stock; normal market forces were not considered likely to provide a stability or level of returns which reflected these long-run or social considerations.

While it is, of course, impossible to show what would have happened without such aids, the relative stability of breeding stock numbers in the late 1960s — when market returns and net farm incomes for hill and upland producers were low — supports the view that these forms of assistance were, in part at least, achieving their purpose. At a political level this view was certainly accepted and the hill grants achieved the status of a 'sticking-point' in the UK's negotiations with the EEC[5] and were eventually enshrined in the approved forms of aid under the Less-Favoured-Areas directive. The special crofting grants (essentially increasing the level of help rather than changing its form), have also received sufficient political support to survive the scrutiny of the Commission.

The case for additional assistance from the Highland Board rested on three main arguments. First it was contended that, within the more traditional

5 During the negotiations the Board took various initiatives designed to strengthen the Government's stand on this issue. Dr Mansholt's first visit to the UK (in 1972) included a visit to the Highlands and a formal meeting with the Board on the consequences of the CAP for Highland agriculture.

livestock sectors of the Highlands, the provision of capital loans at favourable rates was needed to enable some livestock producers to overcome the cash-flow problems involved in land improvement and the associated expansion in stock numbers. The help should be given on a selective basis with the expectation (or at least hope) that the real cost of the 'soft' loan terms and necessary administrative controls would eventually be matched by economic gains in terms of net value-added and social gains in terms of greater stability of the rural population. Secondly, it was suggested that new forms of land use in the Highlands were almost by definition high risk ventures and that some public money should be spent in trying to identify those with a reasonable chance of commercial success — if the impact on local employment and the rural community was considered worthwhile on more general grounds as well. Thirdly, it was argued that within the typical local, social and economic structure of the rural Highlands, there was a case for encouraging a comprehensive approach to development — comprehensive in the sense that State help to forestry, farming or recreational developments within an area should be provided on the basis of an overall, co-ordinated view of how each sector's development might complement the others. Ideally, there would be a 'package deal' between the Board and the users of land which would help to reconcile individual plans with wider social objectives and so achieve a higher level of general welfare for the local community.

It is the nature of theoretical arguments like these to be deficient in empirical evidence until they are acted upon; even then *post hoc ergo propter hoc* is a vulnerable proof to the unconverted. To the cold eye of a dispassionate observer, however, the influence of intellectual argument may in retrospect have counted for less than other factors in convincing the Board (and the Scottish Office) that even a modest regional programme for agriculture was justified. In its early years the Board was criticised for being too concerned with promoting imported large-scale industrial growth at the expense of traditional and indigenous activities, for being 'anti-farming', and for paying too little attention to the interests of the smaller and more rural communities. However unjustified some of these criticisms were thought to be, the Board was not unaffected by them and the case for an agricultural presence was rarely advanced without at least passing reference to such attacks.

Allocating appropriate weights to the various factors which resulted in the Board developing an agricultural programme is not possible; all were influential to some degree. But once a programme was introduced it had to achieve at least a minimum degree of effectiveness to survive. Assessing the total impact of the Board's agricultural and land development programme is obviously impracticable. While it is true that there is some evidence that the relative decline in Highland agricultural employment and output has slowed down over the past 10-15 years, neither the extent nor the main cause of such a development can be reliably associated with any particular aspect of public policy. More confidence can be placed on judgments about the *relative* 'success' or 'failure' of different aspects of the Board's agricultural activities. The capital assistance given to livestock farming, for example, appears to have enabled some producers to reach a higher level of output, incomes and employing capacity than they might otherwise have achieved. But expenditure on new production projects, such as the Uist bulb scheme, has so far failed to achieve any long-term effect on the rural economy, and it may be some time before any non-traditional developments are successful enough to have a substantial impact on productive activity. Support for relatively new forms of livestock marketing has also produced only a very limited effect in a few areas. In general the experience of these activities has confirmed expectations that sections of Highland agriculture outside the main commercial farming areas would present the most difficult development problems.

The land surveys so far completed for selected areas have systematically described and assessed their (limited) potential for development as well as their problems but, more importantly, have focussed public attention on the central issue — in what ways and to what extent should a public body be enabled to implement the development proposals considered desirable for an area showing signs of serious economic and social decline relative to the rest of the country?

For many years controversy has surrounded the extent to which the pattern of land ownership, occupancy and use in the Highlands has hindered the development of desirable land-using activities. Since 1965 the debate has extended to cover different views on the role of the Highlands and Islands Development Board in influencing land use and the most suitable methods for it to adopt. From earlier discussions (see Chapter Two) it will be clear we are in general sympathy with the view that significant areas of land in the Board's area could be used differently and more intensively so as to contribute towards the maintenance of existing rural communities, the production of food and timber and the increase in people's incomes. But general statements on this theme, valid as they may be, will not contribute very much to bringing about such a change. The use of all productive resources — land, labour and capital — could be improved in many sectors of the British economy. What is most necessary, and most convincing, is to show in some detail, and eventually demonstrate in practice, the kind of improvements that could follow from 'better' land use in the Highlands.

The provision of special forms of assistance to potential developers and the direct support of new, risky projects all help to build up social pressures against any persons who, for private reasons, may attempt to use their ownership and control of land to prevent the growth of activities of social and economic benefit to local communities. In addition, development proposals prepared for certain defined areas can also contribute to a climate of opinion in which it is more difficult to justify opposition to changes which are generally accepted as desirable. A development authority must hope that such public pressures will reduce, if not remove, any inhibiting influences arising from existing forms of ownership or control. But it must also recognise the possibility that its own intervention, based on the legislative powers it has been granted, may become an important part of the process of change.

The role a development board can play, however, is not without fairly obvious limitations. It cannot on its own bring about fundamental and widespread changes in, say, the pattern of land ownership unless this can be clearly demonstrated to be necessary to achieve the kind of developments it has been charged to promote. If such changes are considered desirable for other reasons, then Parliament must first be persuaded to provide the means for bringing them about. A development board must adopt a selective approach, seeking to identify areas where existing activities fall significantly short of the potential and to prepare programmes which indicate what can and should be done. Where these proposals meet general approval from local communities but opposition from isolated individuals controlling resources vital to the development — then the Board will be expected to seek to acquire enough of these resources to demonstrate that the proposed programme is likely to have the desired results. Whether such acquisitions are made by voluntary or compulsory purchase (both envisaged in the 1965 Act) the crucial point is that they should be followed by developments that are recognised as desirable and effective. It is thus important that appropriate methods are used to identify the 'right' programmes and to choose the most effective means of implementing them.

Ideally, such methods should show as accurately as possible the costs and benefits likely to be involved in alternative proposals. Thereafter any programme put into effect should be carefully monitored and the results evaluated. Such an approach, it need hardly be said, is not yet an established feature of public development policy in Britain. The few attempts at some kind of cost-benefit appraisal have not been successful enough to encourage its widespread adoption.

The land surveys conducted by the Board (see Chapter Four) were attempts to assess in a systematic way the potential for developement in two areas (Kildonan and Mull) nominated by another public body. These attempts did not profess to make a general cost/benefit analysis of different possible programmes; it became obvious that the nature of the problem and the data available made this impractical. The more limited objective was set of trying to establish whether certain types of land development were feasible, what consequences they might have in regional development terms, what obstacles — if any — were preventing such changes, and what measures the Board might take to encourage any recommended developments.

The carrying out of such surveys, especially when they attempt even a limited economic appraisal of development proposals, is itself a complex and changing process. In our view it is a legitimate function of a regional development board to conduct (or sponsor) such surveys and to attempt to establish practical (and not too expensive) methods of identifying a programme which, if carried out, could be expected to have beneficial economic and social effects which would justify the costs involved. But the technical problems which have to be overcome in establishing the 'right' programme are likely to be much less important than the difficulty of trying to implement it.

A development board can do no more than is politically acceptable at both the national and local level. To illustrate: the Board's proposals for the estate of Killiechronan on Mull appears to have had the support of at least substantial sections of the local community. They did not, however, win approval at central government level and so far there are no obvious signs that greater public involvement in the (voluntary) purchase and development of rural land is likely to be politically and financially acceptable. On the other hand, the Board's attempts to support financially the efforts of other bodies to build up new ways of marketing livestock from outlying areas were conducted in a national policy environment which was generally favourable towards this type of marketing. But there was arguably insufficient support at the local level for establishing the kind of disciplined, well-organised marketing organisation that was necessary to enable this method to have more than a minor impact on this market — easily the most important market for Highland agricultural producers.

Thus to be more successful in implementing an agricultural programme, the Board does not only have to identify the 'right' programme by technical and economic criteria, it must have adequate contacts, understanding and support at local level and a strong political presence at national government level. These are objectives which can be much more readily described than achieved. The Board has only a limited number of officers resident in local areas. It could be that an agricultural programme needs more of that kind of administrative help. Ministerial responsibility for the Board is a more controversial question and a discussion of relations between the Board and the Government of the day would go beyond the scope of this study.

Policy Guidelines

In the context of this study our main concern is with the content of an agricultural development policy rather than with the social, political and administrative environment within which it can operate successfully. With that reservation, the guidelines of policy[6] suggested below set out to cover

6 It may be as well at this point to emphasise what was stated at the outset of this study — although its publication is with the support of the Board the views expressed are the authors' and do not necessarily coincide with the Board's.

its main objectives, the physical and economic conditions within which it is pursued and the link between these aims and conditions and the kind of policy measures proposed.

1 The overall objective of the Board in rural areas in the Highlands and Islands should be to maintain and if possible increase the settled population by helping to provide job opportunities and incomes roughly comparable with other rural parts of the country.

2 Contributing towards this objective should be the more productive use of the land resources of the Highlands by agriculture, forestry and other economic activities which should be developed in a planned and as far as possible complementary relationship to each other.

3 A necessary condition of any land policy measure consistent with these aims should be that it encourages an increase in output and in value-added. If such a condition is fulfilled then the tendency will be to maintain employment in the areas affected at a higher level than would have been likely without assistance. This may not necessarily mean a net addition to employment and in such circumstances there are obvious implications for the development of other (non-land-based) kinds of economic activity.

4 The physical circumstances, present national farm policy and past agricultural developments within the Highlands suggest that some policy measures should specifically relate to cattle and sheep rearing and should aim at removing or minimising the influence of factors which are preventing producers in such enterprises from reaching a higher (but achievable) level of output, technical and economic efficiency and, therefore, income. These measures can include grants and loans and can apply to individual farmers as well as to co-ordinated attempts to improve livestock breeding, fodder production and marketing. Such development measures will by definition exclude assistance which if withdrawn after a reasonable period would mean that producers are forced back on to their former lower level of economic performance; continuing subsidies may be justified in certain conditions but should be the responsibility of national government rather than a regional development agency. The measures should be selective and adequately monitored and their effects should be assessed periodically.

5 In order to exploit any limited comparative advantages which parts of the rural Highlands may hold and to ensure that opportunities offered by technical advances elsewhere are adequately explored, development measures should cover not only established forms of land use but new and (initially) risky enterprises. Such projects will be of an experimental nature in the first instance, and will generally depend on technical expertise from outside the development agency but should gradually take on the character of a commercial development either in co-operation with outside concerns or on behalf of the developing agency itself.

'Ideal' projects will involve a labour-intensive use of land, yield products with a relatively high value to weight and manifest no pronounced economies of scale (above a certain fairly small size of business).

6 The location and structure of present land-based enterprises in the Highlands suggest that a standardised approach in applying certain measures within the region as a whole would be inappropriate. Highland agriculture has at least two sectors and a rigid application of one particular approach could inhibit desirable developments. A balance needs to be struck between meeting the administrative and political requirements of simplicity and equity and achieving a significant impact in the more difficult areas and where farming is likely to remain a part-time occupation. Various techniques can be used to provide such flexibility without going beyond defined limits of financial commitment. In addition special measures taken under national or EEC support schemes — such as the Less Favoured Areas directive — could provide differential support for particularly difficult parts of the region.

7 While a 'Highland Plan' for the general development of all land-based activities in the region might become, in practice, little more than a statement of general objectives and production targets, at a more local level the concept of a comprehensive approach to such developments could have an operational effect. The existence of several public bodies with their own (sometimes narrowly-defined) functions is bound to create problems of co-ordination; a regional body is required to take an overall view and to seek ways of persuading other organisations to subordinate their special interests to wider objectives. To secure implementation of such a comprehensive plan for an area will therefore require the Board to be accorded a co-ordinating function; it will also require strong support from the local community.

8 Central to any programme of regional agricultural development will be means for influencing the use of land. As a general rule the measures used are likely to be economic and financial rather than administrative, grants and loans rather than direct intervention. But exercising control over the use of land, which is already accepted when some changes in use are proposed, may well emerge as a precondition for the success of certain aspects of an agricultural development programme. A regional development authority should therefore have powers and finance to acquire land, preferably on a voluntary basis but if necessary by compulsion, when this is essential to achieve approved objectives of land development. The legal means for doing so should be based on the conditions within which rural (as distinct from urban) developments normally take place.

9 As a general principle which should be refelected in all aspects of policy, the objectives of different measures should be defined with sufficient clarity to ensure that at some stage in the future it will be possible to

decide whether or not they have been achieved. The well known difficulties of measuring the extent of any policy impact should not prevent a judgment being made of the direction in which change has taken place.

In conclusion it may be wise to re-emphasise a point which has been made several times. However desirable the above objectives may be, their achievement will obviously depend on many other factors than the relatively small financial contribution which the Board, as a development authority, can make to agriculture in the Highlands. The roles of Central Government, of public bodies like the Crofters Commission, Forestry Commission, Agricultural Colleges, are all of great influence. The impact of EEC policies could also be very important. The Board will therefore be concerned not only with the allocation of its own funds but with the need to ensure that the activities of all bodies with a responsibility in Highland agriculture and land use are consistent with achieving for the rural communities that increase in the 'social well-being and development' of the region that the 1965 Act was designed to promote.

Bibliography

ABERDEEN UNIVERSITY (1973) — *Economic Survey of Private Forestry: Income and Expenditure, Scotland 1961-73*, Aberdeen, 1974.

ADVISORY PANEL ON THE HIGHLANDS AND ISLANDS (1964) — *Report*, HMSO, 1964.

ANDERSON, M L (1967) — *A History of Scottish Forestry, Vol 2*, Nelson, Edinburgh and London, 1967.

BIBBY, J S (1973) — *Land Capability*, Ch 5 in Tivy J (ed) (1973).

BIBBY, J S and MACKNEY, D (1969) — *Land Use Capability Classification*, Soil Survey, Technical Monograph No 1, Rothamstead, Herts, and Macaulay Institute, Aberdeen, 1969.

BICKMORE, D P and SHAW, M A (1963) — *The Atlas of Great Britain and Northern Ireland*, Oxford University Press, 1963.

BIRCHMORE, M J and McDONAGH, P A (1973) — *The Employment Generating Effect of Primary Forestry Investment in a District of Argyllshire*. Unpublished Report to HIDB.

BLAND, G H M (1969) — *The Potential Market for Venison and its Possible Operations* in Bannerman, M M and Blaxter, K L (ed) (1969). *The Husbanding of Red Deer, Proceedings of a Conference Held at the Rowett Institute, Aberdeen, in January 1969*, Rowett Institute and HIDB, 1969.

BLAXTER, K L, CUNNINGHAM, J M M, et al (1974) — *Farming the Red Deer*, HMSO, Edinburgh, 1974.

BURT (1754) — *Letters from a Gentleman in the North of Scotland* (London 1754) II. p 55. Cited in Smout, TC (1969).

CAIRD, J B (1972) — *Changes in the Highlands and Islands of Scotland 1951-71*, Geo Forum 12, 1972.

CASON, R G (1968) — *Sources and Allocation of Capital for Investment in Agriculture*, North of Scotland College of Agriculture, Economic Report No 129, 1968.

CLERK, D (1881) — Trans. H and A. Soc. Scot. pp 227-228, 1881.

COLLIER, A (1953) — *The Crofting Problem*, Cambridge University Press.

CROFTERS COMMISSION (1972) — *Annual Report 1972*, HMSO Edinburgh, 1973.

CROFTERS COMMISSION (1974) — *Annual Report 1974*, HMSO, Edinburgh, 1975.

CUNNINGHAM, J M M (1974) — *The Biological Resources of the Highlands*. Paper to the British Association for the Advancement of Science Meeting, Stirling, 1974. Published in the *Annual Report* of the Highland Fund 1974/75.

CUNNINGHAM, J M M and BLAXTER, K L (1974) — *Farming the Red Deer, The First Report of An Investigation by the Rowett Research Institute and the Hill Farming Research Organisation*, HMSO, Edinburgh, 1974.

DEPARTMENT OF AGRICULTURE AND FISHERIES FOR SCOTLAND — *Agricultural Statistics*, 1951-74 Scotland, HMSO, Edinburgh. *Machinery Census*, HMSO, Edinburgh. *June Census Returns*, 1958-74, HMSO, Edinburgh.

DARLING, F F (1955) — *West Highland Survey: An Essay in Human Ecology*, Oxford University Press, 1955.

DEAN, R (1966) — *Bulbs for the Western Isles*, HIDB, Inverness, 1966.

DEER FORESTS COMMITTEE (1912) — *Report of the Departmental Committee on Deer Forests*, 1912. (1922) — *Report of the Departmental Committee on Deer Forests*, 1922.

FIRST (OLD) STATISTICAL ACCOUNT OF SCOTLAND (1790-1800).

FORESTRY COMMISSION — *Annual Reports*, 1969-70 to 1972-73 incl, HMSO, London.

GENERAL REGISTER OFFICE — *Population Census* 1871, 1911, 1931, 1951, 1961, 1966 and 1971, HMSO, Edinburgh.

GLOYNE, R W (1973) — *Crop Production in Higher Latitudes, Maritime Areas*, Int. J. Biometeor. 1973, Vol 17, No 4.
GREEN, F H W (1974) — *Changes in Artificial Drainage, Fertilisers and Climate in Scotland*, J. of Environmental Man, 1974 (2).
GREEN, F H W (1975) — *The Transient Snow-line in the Scottish Highlands*, 'Weather' July 1975.
GREGORY, S (1954) — *'Climate'*, in *British Isles: A Systematic Geography*, Ed. by Watson, J W and Sissons, J B, Nelson, Edinburgh, 1964.
GRIEVE, R (1968) — *Address to the Seventh Highlands and Islands Conference Organised by the STUC*, November 1968.

HALDANE, A R B (1951) — *The Drove Roads of Scotland*, Nelson, London, 1957.
HANDLEY, J E (1953) — *Scottish Farming in the 18th Century*, Faber, 1953.
HANSARD (March 1965) — Cols 1088/1089.
HIGHLANDS AND ISLANDS DEVELOPMENT BOARD (1966) — *First Annual Report 1966*, HIDB, Inverness, 1967. (1971) — *Sixth Annual Report 1971*, HIDB, Inverness, 1972. (1973) — *Eighth Annual Report 1973*, HIDB, Inverness, 1974. (1970) — *Occasional Bulletin No 2*, HIDB, Inverness, August 1970. (1970) — *Strath of Kildonan — Proposals for Development*, Special Report No 5, HIDB, Inverness, 1970. (1973) — *Island of Mull — Survey and Proposals for Development*, Special Report No 10, HIDB, Inverness, 1973.
HILL FARMING RESEARCH ORGANISATION (1975) — *Lephinmore Research Station Handbook*, HFRO, 1975.
HILL LANDS (NORTH OF SCOTLAND) COMMISSION (1956) — *Cmnd 9759*, HMSO, 1956.
HUNT, I V (1973) — *The Grass Crop*, Ch 10 in Tivy, J (ed) (1973).
HUNTER, T (1883) — *Woods, Forests and Estates in Perthshire*, Perth, 1883.

INSTITUTE OF GEOLOGICAL SCIENCES (1960) — Geological Maps.

JACK HOLMES PLANNING GROUP (1968) — *The Moray Firth — A Plan for Growth in a Sub-region of the Scottish Highlands*, Prepared for the HIDB, London, 1968.
JOINT ADVISORY COMMITTEE ON AGRICULTURAL EDUCATION (1973) — *('Hudson Report)*, HMSO, 1973.
JOWSEY, P C (1973) — *Peatlands*, Ch 9 in Tivy, J (ed) (1973).
LOCKIE, J D and McVEAN, D (1969) — *Ecology and Land Use in Upland Scotland*, Edinburgh University Press, Edinburgh, 1969.

MANLEY, G (1952) — *Climate and the British Scene*, Collins, London, 1952.
MATHER, A (1972) — Appendix to the *Annual Report of the Red Deer Commission*, 1972, HMSO 1973.
METEOROLOGICAL OFFICE — *Monthly Weather Reports*, Vols 88 and 89, HMSO. *Hydrological Memo*, No 37, HMSO.
MILLER, R (1973) — *Bioclimatic Characteristics*, Ch 2 in Tivy, J (ed) (1973).
MILLMAN, R N (1969) — *The Marches of the Highland Estates*, Scottish Geographical Magazine, Vol 85, No 3.
MILLMAN, R N (1970) — *The Landed Properties of Northern Scotland*, Scottish Geographical Magazine, Vol 86, No 3, 1970.
MILLMAN, R N (1971) — *Outdoor Recreation in the Highland Countryside — A Study of Rural Management and Access for Public Recreation in 10 Selected Areas of the Highlands and Islands*, Cambridge, 1971.
McDIARMID, A (1969) — *Diseases of Red Deer and their Possible Significance in Deer Farming Projects, Veterinary Preventive Medicine and Public Health*, in Bannerman, M M and Blaxter, K L (ed) (1969).
MacDONALD, J (1811) — *General View of the Agriculture of the Hebrides*, Cited in Haldane (1951).
McEWAN, L V (1971) — *Capital in Scottish Agriculture*, Scottish Agricultural Economics, Vol XXI, 1971.
McEWEN, J (1975) — *Highland Landlordism*, in Brown (ed) *The Red Paper on Scotland*, EUSPB Edinburgh, 1975.
MacKAY, D I and BUXTON, N K (1965) — *The North of Scotland Economy: A case for Redevelopment*, Scottish Journal of Political Economy, Vol 12, 1965.
MacKENZIE, A M (1973) — *Capital Expenditure — Analysis of Data from the Farm Capital*

Grants Scheme, SAE, Vol XXIII, 1973.
MacKENZIE, A M (1974) — *Agricultural Land Prices — Scotland*, SAE, Vol XXIV, 1974.
MacKENZIE, A M (1965) — *Agricultural Output in Scotland by Regions 1961/62* SAE, Vol XV, 1965.
MacKENZIE, A M, MARTIN P C and SCARLETT, E R (1975) — *Agricultural Output of Scotland by Regions*, SAE, Vol XXV, 1975.
MacLEAN, D (1905) — *Descriptions of Shootings and Fishings, the Property of the Duke of Sutherland*, Golspie, 1905. Cited in O'Dell, A C and Walton, K (1962) — *The Highlands and Islands of Scotland*, Nelson, London and Edinburgh, 1962.

NATURAL RESOURCES (TECHNICAL) COMMITTEE (1957) — *Report on Land Use in the Highlands and Islands*, HMSO, 1964.
NORTH OF SCOTLAND COLLEGE OF AGRICULTURE (1971) — *Farm Business Management Handbook*, 1971. — *An Agro-Economic Appraisal of Agriculture in Easter Ross*, Economic Report No 121, July 1967.

O'DELL, A C and WALTON, K (1962) — *The Highlands and Islands of Scotland*, Nelson, London and Edinburgh, 1962.
ORMISTON, J H (1973) — *The Moray Firth: An Agricultural Study*, HIDB Special Report No 9, HIDB, Inverness, April 1973.

PLANT, J A (1970) — The Climate of the Coastal Region of the Moray Firth, Met Office Climatological Memo No 62, 1970.

RAGG, J M (1973) — *Factors in Soil Formation*, Ch 4 in Tivy, J (ed) (1973).
RED DEER COMMISSION — *Annual Reports* 1970-73 incl. HMSO.

SCOTTISH AGRICULTURAL ECONOMICS — Vol V, 1954. — Vol XV, 1965. — The Financial Results of Scottish Farming 1972-3, Vol XXIV, 1974. — Vol XXV, 1975.
SELECT COMMITTEE ON LAND USE (1963) — *Report*, HMSO, 1963.
SELECT COMMITTEE ON SCOTTISH AFFAIRS 1971-72 — *Land Resource Use in Scotland*, Vol III, London, HMSO 1972.
SIMPSON, D (1963) — *Investment, Employment and Government Expenditure in the Highlands, 1951-60*, Scottish Journal of Political Economy, Vol X, November 1963.
SINCLAIR, SIR J (ed) (1814) — *General Report of the Agricultural State and Political Circumstances of Scotland*, 5 vols, 1814.
SMITH, REV J (1798) — *General View of the Agriculture of the County of Argyll*, 1798.
SMOUT, T C (1969) — *A History of the Scottish People 1560-1830*, Collins, 1969.
STATISTICAL ACCOUNT OF SCOTLAND (NEW) — 15 vols, 1845.
STEWART, I M T (1965) — *Capital in Scottish Agriculture*, SAE, Vol XV, 1965.
SWAN, W B and SENIOR, W H (1973) — *Survey of Agriculture in Caithness, Orkney and Shetland*, Special Report No 8, HIDB, Inverness, 1973.
SYMON, J A (1959) — *Scottish Farming, Past and Present*, Oliver and Boyd, Edinburgh, 1959.

TIVY, J (ed) (1973) — *The Organic Resources of Scotland: Their Nature and Evaluation*, Oliver and Boyd, Edinburgh, 1973.
TRANS. H & A SOC. SCOT. — 1878-1938.

WAGSTAFF, H R (1970) — *Scotland's Farm Occupiers*, SAE, Vol XX, 1970.
WAISTER, P D (1973) — *Climatic Limitations on Horticultural Production with Particular Reference to Scottish Conditions*, Int. J. Biometeor, 1973, Vol 17, No 4.
WATSON, W J and SISSONS, J B (1964) — *British Isles: a Systematic Geography*, Nelson, Edinburgh and London, 1964.
WILSON, J S G (1973) — *Availability of Capital and Credit to UK Agriculture*, London, HMSO, 1973.
WOLFE, J N and CABORN, J M (1973) — *Some Considerations Regarding Forestry Policy in Great Britain*, Forestry Committee of Great Britain, April 1973.

YOUNGSON, A J (1973) — *After the Forty-Five. The Economic Impact on the Scottish Highlands*, Edinburgh University Press, Edinburgh, 1973.

Index